MONSTER 500 PUZZLE CHALLENGE

General Editor: Robert Allen

SEVENOAKS

Design copyright © Carlton Books Ltd 2004

Unless otherwise stated all puzzles © 2004 Puzzler Media Limited, RH1 1EY, www.puzzler.co.uk

The following puzzles are the copyright of Conceptis Puzzles (http://www.conceptis.tech.com):
puzzles number 8, 29, 33, 38, 41, 42, 50, 55, 59, 62, 64, 65, 66, 67, 68, 76, 77, 79, 80, 81, 83, 87, 89, 90, 92, 93, 94, 95, 96, 97, 104, 105, 107, 108, 115, 126, 132, 133, 143, 147, 154, 157, 168, 170, 176, 188, 190, 215, 225, 232, 236, 246, 253, 260, 270, 282, 291, 301, 311, 315, 322, 328, 334, 336, 339, 345, 347, 354, 356, 360, 365, 368, 371, 377, 384, 400, 404, 405, 409, 415, 418, 420, 426, 428, 434, 440, 447, 450, 454, 462, 470, 478, 483, 489, 496, 498

This edition published in 2006 by SevenOaks
A Division of the Carlton Publishing Group
20 Mortimer Street
London W1T 3JW

A CIP catalogue record for this book is available from the British Library.

ISBN 13: 978-0-681-15485-8
ISBN 10: 0-681-15485-3

Art Director: Clare Baggaley
Design: Q2A and Sooky Choi
Production: Lisa Moore

Printed in Dubai

INTRODUCTION

Puzzling is one of life's great pleasures. It is also one of the oldest. Did you know that puzzles have been discovered as far back as the days when Ur and Babylon were major powers in the world? Yes, the urge to set and solve puzzles goes right back to the dawn of civilisation. You know the one about, 'As I was travelling to St Ives I met a man with seven wives?' That is actually a modernised version of a puzzle found in the ruins of Babylon! So when you are doing puzzles, you are part of an ancient and honourable tradition of mental gymnastics.

Sadly many people are not only blind to the fascination of puzzles, but would also dearly like to spoil the fun for everyone else. Have you ever been told by friends or relatives that solving puzzles is just a waste of time? They don't know what they're talking about! Did you know that the latest medical research suggests strongly that puzzling is actually good for you? It's true! People who solve puzzles are significantly less likely to suffer from dementia as they grow older. They are far more likely to remain bright, alert and in good mental shape because they engaged in this fascinating and stimulating hobby. So just tell that to anyone who doubts that puzzling is a good way to spend your spare time. In addition, doing puzzles does no harm to anyone and costs very little money.

We have given each puzzle a difficulty rating (the more stars in the heading, the harder the puzzle), but don't be put off by a three-star rating, as what we found difficult may be a breeze for you. So turn the page, kick back and have fun with the 500 puzzles we have selected for you.

1 LEFT, RIGHT ★

Two of the pictures are identical, whilst each of the others differs in one small detail. Which are the 'twins', and what are the differences?

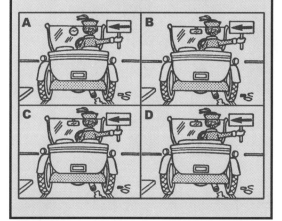

3 ABC ★★

Each line, across and down, is to have each of the letters A, B and C, and two empty squares. The letter outside the grid shows the first or second letter in the direction of the arrow. Can you fill in the grid?

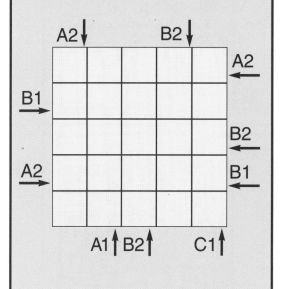

2 INSTRU-MENTAL ★★★

The five members of the Trout Quintet also double up on another instrument when playing jazz instead of Mozart. Taking your cue from the drummer, can you take note of the clues and play out a summary giving the full name and home town of each instrumentalist?

1 Honour plays the viola. Pearl plays the clarinet but not the harp. Des Kant is the drummer.

2 Harris plays the piano but not the violin. Janice plays the oboe but not the bass or harp.

3 The violin player comes from Fife but is not Tewitt or Tring neither of whom plays the clarinet.

4 Tring is not Nathan who is the banjo player but is not from Derby. Heyer comes from Rhyll. The cellist comes from Wells.

INSTRUMENT		FORENAME	SURNAME	FROM
BASS		DES	HARRIS	DERBY
		HONOUR	HEYER	FIFE
		JANICE	KANT	PENGE
		NATHAN	TEWITT	RHYLL
		PEARL	TRING	WELLS
CELLO		DES	HARRIS	DERBY
		HONOUR	HEYER	FIFE
		JANICE	KANT	PENGE
		NATHAN	TEWITT	RHYLL
		PEARL	TRING	WELLS
HARP		DES	HARRIS	DERBY
		HONOUR	HEYER	FIFE
		JANICE	KANT	PENGE
		NATHAN	TEWITT	RHYLL
		PEARL	TRING	WELLS
VIOLA		DES	HARRIS	DERBY
		HONOUR	HEYER	FIFE
		JANICE	KANT	PENGE
		NATHAN	TEWITT	RHYLL
		PEARL	TRING	WELLS
VIOLIN		DES	HARRIS	DERBY
		HONOUR	HEYER	FIFE
		JANICE	KANT	PENGE
		NATHAN	TEWITT	RHYLL
		PEARL	TRING	WELLS

4   PILE UP

These piles of bricks aren't the random results of a child's play but clues to a final, at present blank, pile on the right. Like the rest, that one has six bricks each with a different one of the six letters. The numbers below the heaps tell you two things:

(a) The number of adjacent pairs of bricks in that column which also appear adjacent in the final pile.

(b) The number of adjacent pairs of bricks that make a correct pair but the wrong way up.

So:

would score one in the 'Correct' row if the final heap had an A directly above a C and a one in the 'Reversed' row if the final heap had a C on top of an A. From all this, can you create the final pile before it topples?

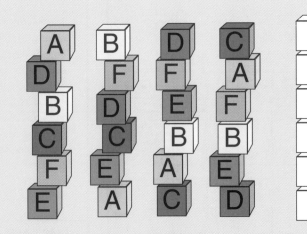

| Correct | 1 | 1 | 1 | 2 | 5 |
| Reversed | 0 | 0 | 0 | 0 | 0 |

5   CLUELESS

Can you find the detail missing in each picture that is present in the other three?

6 CARDS ON THE TABLE

The 13 cards of a suit are shuffled and dealt out in a row, and it is found that none is in its correct numerical position (Ace left, King right), and the court cards are not at either end or adjacent to each other. The Ace is between 9 (left) and 8, 4 between Queen (left) and Jack, 2 two places left of 10, 7 two places left of 3, the left end card one higher than the right end card, and the King is left of the Queen. The 9th and 10th cards from the left total 9, the 9th being of lower value. Can you locate each card?

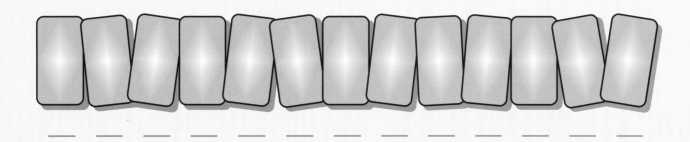

7 NUMBER JIG

Fit the numbers into the grid as quickly as possible. One has been done for you.

3 figures

178
212
375
575
(604)
619
715
830

4 figures

1802
2124
2991
3017
3201
4000
4057
5000
5588
6048

6543
7142
7891
8106
8341
9012
9867

5 figures

13275
14448
15290
21543
37465
43125
45678
45687
51279
57267
65432
70000
71847

81736
87653
90103
98314

6 figures

140747
190668
555855
626206
754321
846684

8 TSUNAMI

The numbers alongside each row or column tell you how many blocks of black squares are in a line. For example: 2, 3, 5 tells you that from left to right (or top to bottom) there is a group of two black squares, then at least one white space, then a group of three black squares, then at least one white shape, then a group of five black squares. Each block of black squares on the same line must have at least one white square between it and the next block of black squares.

Sometimes it is possible to tell which squares are going to be black without reference to other lines or columns. In the example below, we can deduce that any block of six black squares must incorporate the two central squares:

Can you complete this tsunami puzzle, to reveal the hidden pattern or picture?

Row clues (top to bottom):
- 4
- 5 6
- 7 8
- 4 3 1 4
- 3 2 1 1 4
- 3 1 1 2 1 3
- 3 2 2 3
- 3 2 2 1 2 1
- 4 2 3 2 3
- 4 1 3 1 3
- 5 4 2 1 2
- 3 1 1 3 3 2 1
- 2 1 1 2 3 2
- 1 1 1 1 2 1 3
- 1 1 1 2 1 4
- 1 1 1 1 1 11
- 1 1 1 1 11
- 1 1 1 1 1 6
- 1 1 6 5
- 1 1 2 5 1
- 1 1 1 5 2
- 5 1 1 3
- 1 4 12
- 6 1 13
- 1 3 14
- 2 7 10
- 4 13
- 5 8 4
- 7 5 2
- 9 8

9 PILE UP ★★

These piles of bricks aren't the random results of a child's play but clues to a final, at present blank, pile on the right. Like the rest, that one has six bricks each with a different one of the six letters. The numbers below the heaps tell you two things:
(a) The number of adjacent pairs of bricks in that column which also appear adjacent in the final pile.
(b) The number of adjacent pairs of bricks that make a correct pair but the wrong way up.
So:

 would score one in the 'Correct' row if the final heap had an A directly above a C and a one in the 'Reversed' row if the final heap had a C on top of an A. From all this, can you create the final pile before it topples?

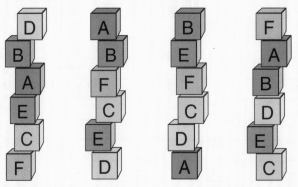
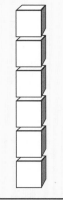

Correct	2	0	0	0	5
Reversed	0	0	0	1	0

10 DOMINO SEARCH

A standard set of dominoes has been laid out, using numbers instead of dots for clarity. Using a sharp pencil and a keen brain, can you draw in the lines to show where each domino has been placed? You may find the check grid useful – crossing off each domino as you find it.

6	4	5	3	3	3	4	5
0	0	6	6	0	3	2	1
3	0	2	5	2	6	4	2
6	1	3	2	2	5	5	1
0	6	0	5	0	4	3	1
5	4	1	5	0	2	4	4
4	1	2	1	3	6	1	6

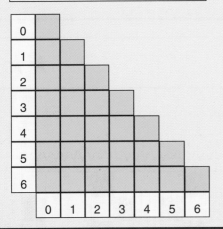

12 LOGI-5

Can you place the letters A, B, C, D, E, one to each square, so that every line across and down has each letter once and every shape made from five squares also has each letter once?

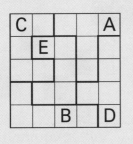

11 CAUGHT NAPPING

Solve the clues given to find out the facts about five murderers who might well have 'got away with it' except for an odd twist of fate - sometimes their own folly. For instance, after committing a murder on a train, one man accidentally left behind his own hat and took the victim's! Another poisoned his wife, successfully, but then his friends, in meals, making them ill and leading to his arrest. Read on! The first clue has been entered for you.

1 Franz Muller died earlier than the murderer caught napping, not only because of his handwriting, but also because he missed the P out of Hampstead in a note. Armstrong died the decade before Frederick.

2 Field confessed to two murders he didn't commit to gain money from newspapers. The first time he was freed, but the second time he was believed - and hung! He was not one of the first two of the five to die.

3 Manton, who died in 1947, was not Herbert, the poisoner.

4 Horace was not the one who died in 1949 after being convicted on the evidence of the only identifiable part of the remains of the victim's body – a gallstone!

HINT:
In which year did Field die? So who died in 1949?

FIRST NAME	SURNAME	YEAR DIED	CONVICTION
FRANZ	ARMSTRONG	1864	CONFESSION
	FIELD	1922	GALLSTONE
	HAIG	1936	HAT
	MANTON	1947	POISON
	MULLER	1949	SPELLING
FREDERICK	ARMSTRONG	1864	CONFESSION
	FIELD	1922	GALLSTONE
	HAIG	1936	HAT
	MANTON	1947	POISON
	MULLER	1949	SPELLING
HERBERT	ARMSTRONG	1864	CONFESSION
	FIELD	1922	GALLSTONE
	HAIG	1936	HAT
	MANTON	1947	POISON
	MULLER	1949	SPELLING
HORACE	ARMSTRONG	1864	CONFESSION
	FIELD	1922	GALLSTONE
	HAIG	1936	HAT
	MANTON	1947	POISON
	MULLER	1949	SPELLING
JOHN	ARMSTRONG	1864	CONFESSION
	FIELD	1922	GALLSTONE
	HAIG	1936	HAT
	MANTON	1947	POISON
	MULLER	1949	SPELLING

13 ABC ★★

Each line, across and down, is to have each of the letters A, B and C, and two empty squares. The letter outside the grid shows the first or second letter in the direction of the arrow. Can you fill in the grid?

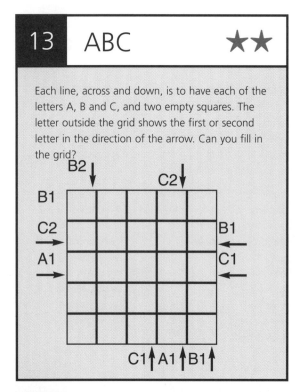

14 BALANCING THE SCALES ★★

How many circles are needed to balance scale C?

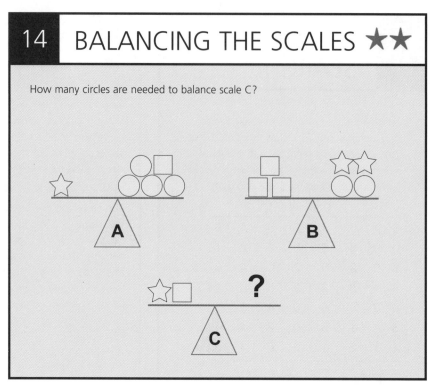

15 DATELINE ★★

This is an odd type of safe. If you solve all the clues and enter them in the grid, the correct combination will appear in the shaded squares.

ACROSS
1 Boiling point in Fahrenheit
3 Multiply 16 by 14
5 Subtract *12 down* from 15 cubed
7 Roman XXIX in figures
8 Divide *24 down* by *7 across*
9 Add one score to *28 across*
11 Double the square of 11
13 26 per cent of 1,650
14 Feet in 3,673 yards
16 Multiply *33 across* by *26 down*
21 Subtract *19 down* from *16 across*
22 Cube Buchan's steps
25 Multiply *31 across* by 57
27 Quadruple the reverse digits of *25 across*
28 Square root of 376,996
30 Subtract 9,000 from one-fourteenth of *20 down*
31 Baker's dozen
32 Multiply 12 by 44
33 Subtract yards in a mile from *1 down*
34 Add *5 across* to *11 across*

DOWN
1 Inches in 641 hands
2 Cube 61
4 Subtract 7 from 10 times *7 across*
5 Minutes in 3 days
6 Add cube of 8 to cube of 9
9 Square of *1 down*
10 Seven-ninths of 5,360,418
12 Ounces in 185 pounds
15 Subtract half a dozen from treble *18 down*
17 Multiply Snow White's dwarfs by *4 down*
18 Add *1 across* to one-fifth of 2,035
19 Subtract *1 down* from *14 across*
20 Multiply *28 across* by *3 across*
23 Days in 27 leap years
24 319 dozen
26 Square feet in 113 square yards
29 Yards in 5 chains

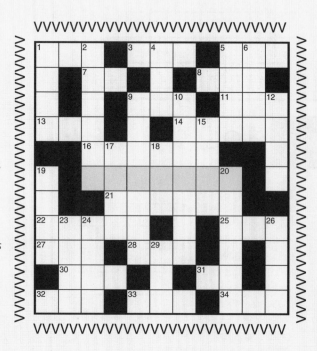

16 THAT LITTLE BIT OF DIFFERENCE ★

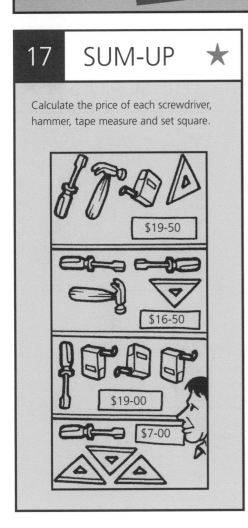

There are eight differences between the two cartoons. Can you spot them?

17 SUM-UP ★

Calculate the price of each screwdriver, hammer, tape measure and set square.

$19-50

$16-50

$19-00

$7-00

18 FIGUREWORK ★★

Fit the figures into the grid as quickly as possible. We have given you a 5-figure number to start you off.

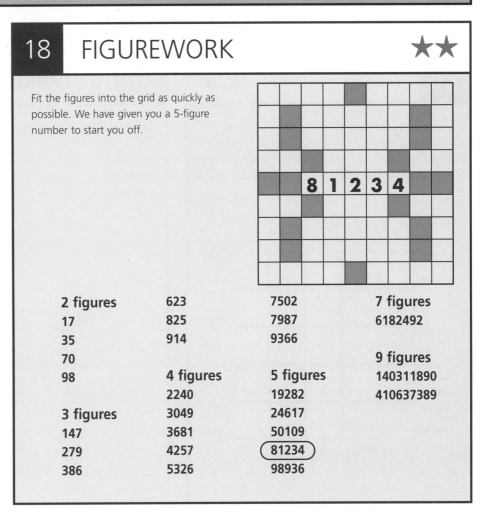

8 1 2 3 4

2 figures	623	7502	7 figures
17	825	7987	6182492
35	914	9366	
70			9 figures
98	4 figures	5 figures	140311890
	2240	19282	410637389
3 figures	3049	24617	
147	3681	50109	
279	4257	81234	
386	5326	98936	

19   PILE UP

These piles of bricks aren't the random results of a child's play but clues to a final, at present blank, pile on the right. Like the rest, that one has six bricks each with a different one of the six letters. The numbers below the heaps tell you two things:

(a) The number of adjacent pairs of bricks in that column which also appear adjacent in the final pile.

(b) The number of adjacent pairs of bricks that make a correct pair but the wrong way up.

So:

 would score one in the 'Correct' row if the final heap had an A directly above a C and a one in the 'Reversed' row if the final heap had a C on top of an A. From all this, can you create the final pile before it topples?

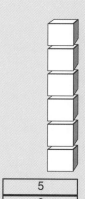

Correct	1	0	0	0		5
Reversed	0	0	2	2		0

20   ABC   ★★

Each line, across and down, is to have each of the letters A. B and C, and two empty squares. The letter outside the grid shows the first or second letter in the direction of the arrow. Can you fill in the grid?

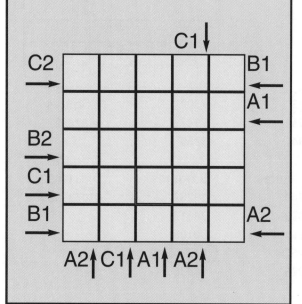

21   BALANCING THE SCALES ★★

How many circles are needed to balance scale C?

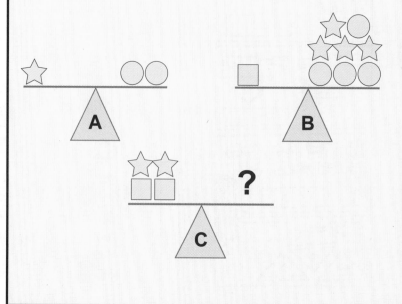

22 BATTLE ZONE ★

Can you find the detail in each picture that is missing from the other three?

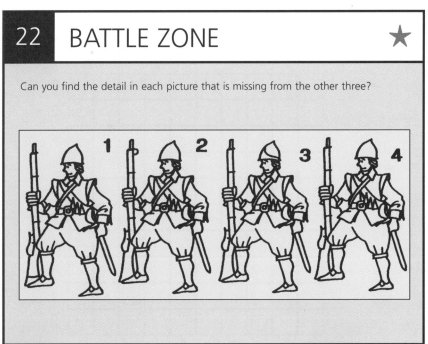

23 IDENTIGRIDS ★

Which three squares are exactly the same? Be careful, they are not necessarily the same way up!

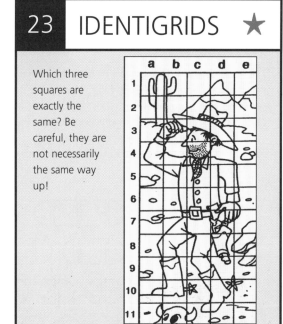

24 FRAME FIVE ★

Can you see which five squares of the picture have been reproduced on the right? Watch out – they might not be the same way up!

25 LOGI-PATH ★★

Use your deductive reasoning to form a pathway from the box marked START to the box marked FINISH moving in either direction horizontally or vertically (but not diagonally). The number at the beginning of every row or column indicates exactly how many boxes in that row or column your pathway must pass through. The small diagram is given as an example of how it works.

26. BATTLESHIPS

Do you remember the old game of battleships? These puzzles are based on that idea. Your task is to find the vessels in the diagram. Some parts of boats or sea squares have already been filled in, and a number next to a row or column refers to the number of occupied squares in that row or column. The boats may be positioned horizontally or vertically, but no two boats or parts of boats are in adjacent squares – horizontally, vertically or diagonally.

Aircraft carrier:

Battleships:

Cruisers:

Destroyers:

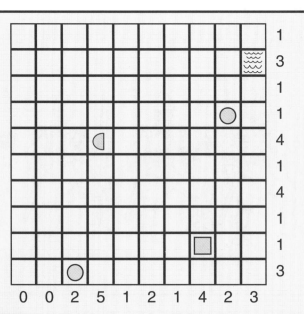

Row totals (top to bottom): 1 3 1 1 4 1 4 1 1 3

Column totals (left to right): 0 0 2 5 1 2 1 4 2 3

27 FRAME-UP ★

Paul took a photograph of his girlfriend in the aviary at the local zoo. Which bird in the aviary is the same as the one in the photograph?

28 SAFE BET

This is an odd type of safe. If you solve all the clues and enter them in the grid, the correct combination will appear in the shaded squares.

ACROSS

1 Multiply *29 across* by 100, then add *9 across*
3 Subtract 2,356 from *21 across*
5 Add 10 to *9 across*
6 Add 34 to *22 down*, then multiply by 3
9 Divide *10 down* by 24
11 Square root of 1,022,121
13 Subtract 811 from *3 across*
15 Square *1 down*
19 Square *3 across*
21 Add 1,022 to *22 down*
23 Multiply *9 across* by 87
25 Add 1 to *5 across*
26 Multiply *3 across* by 3,

then multiply by 10
29 First two digits of *10 down*
30 Twice *3 across*
31 Subtract 9 from *3 across*

DOWN

1 Multiply the last digit of *20 down* by 265
2 Add 80 to *3 down*
3 Last three digits of *1 down*
4 3 per cent of 300,600
5 Subtract 30 from *18 down*
6 5 per cent of 22,839,100
7 Subtract 2,754,362 from *19 across*

8 Subtract 34,945 from *6 down*
10 Subtract 8,730 from *4 down*
12 Add 3 to *9 across*, then multiply by 989
14 Add 309 to *6 across*
16 Add 459 to *17 down*
17 Add 312 to *20 down*
18 Subtract *30 across* from *24 down*
20 First three digits of *12 down*
22 Square root of 11,108,889
24 Twice *1 down*
27 Add 187 to *28 down*
28 Next in series 424, 523, 622 …

29 TSUNAMI

The numbers alongside each row or column tell you how many blocks of black squares are in a line. For example: 2, 3, 5 tells you that from left to right (or top to bottom) there is a group of two black squares, then at least one white space, then a group of three black squares, then at least one white shape, then a group of five black squares. Each block of black squares on the same line must have at least one white square between it and the next block of black squares.

Sometimes it is possible to tell which squares are going to be black without reference to other lines or columns. In the example below, we can deduce that any block of six black squares must incorporate the two central squares:

6

Can you complete this tsunami puzzle, to reveal the hidden pattern or picture?

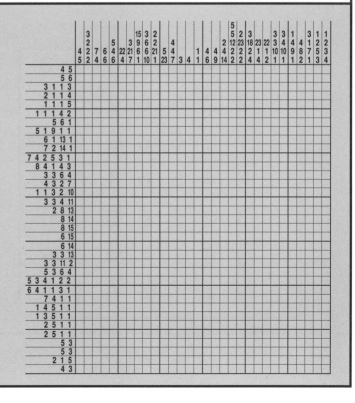

30   ABC   ★★

Each line, across and down, is to have each of the letters A, B and C, and two empty squares. The letter outside the grid shows the first or second letter in the direction of the arrow. Can you fill in the grid?

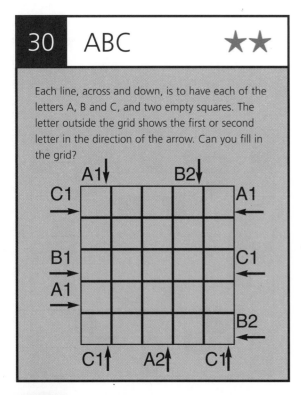

31   BALANCING THE SCALES ★★

How many circles are needed to balance C?

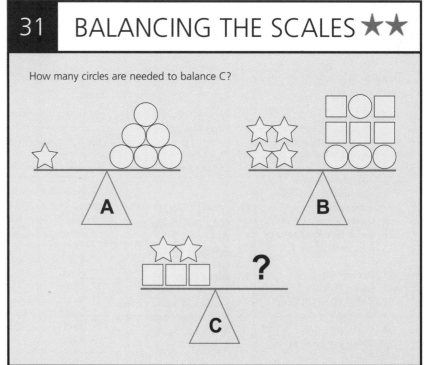

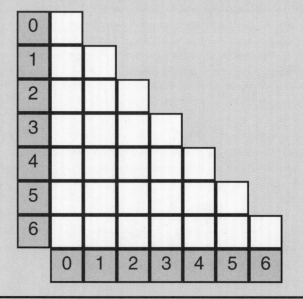

32   DOMINO SEARCH   ★★

A standard set of dominoes has been laid out, using numbers instead of dots for clarity. Using a sharp pencil and a keen brain, can you draw in the lines to show where each domino has been placed? You may find the check grid useful – crossing off each domino as you find it.

1	2	4	5	1	1	1	3
6	2	2	5	6	2	5	3
2	1	2	5	6	3	6	3
2	6	4	5	0	4	0	4
0	3	0	5	6	0	0	0
5	3	6	5	4	4	6	3
3	1	4	1	4	0	1	2

33 TSUNAMI ★★

The numbers alongside each row or column tell you how many blocks of black squares are in a line. For example: 2, 3, 5 tells you that from left to right (or top to bottom) there is a group of two black squares, then at least one white space, then a group of three black squares, then at least one white shape, then a group of five black squares. Each block of black squares on the same line must have at least one white square between it and the next block of black squares.

Sometimes it is possible to tell which squares are going to be black without reference to other lines or columns. In the example below, we can deduce that any block of six black squares must incorporate the two central squares:

6					■	■				

Can you complete this tsunami puzzle, to reveal the hidden pattern or picture?

	2 1 1 2	1 1 1 2	1 1 1 2	1 1 1 1	1 1 4 1 1	5 2 7 2	1 2 1 1 1 3 1	1 2 3 2 3 1	1 1 3 4 1	1 1 1 3 3	1 1 1 4 4	1 1 8 3	1 1 6 3 2	3 2 6 3	1 4 2 3
8															
1 1															
1 5															
6															
2 3															
1 2															
1 2 8															
1 5 4															
5 2 2 1															
1 2 1															
1 3 3															
1 4															
1 1 2 1															
2 4 3 1															
2 1 3 3															
3 5 4															
2 4 3															
6 2															
1 2 3															
7 3															

34 PILE UP ★★

These piles of bricks aren't the random results of a child's play but clues to a final, at present blank, pile on the right. Like the rest, that one has six bricks each with a different one of the six letters. The numbers below the heaps tell you two things:

(a) The number of adjacent pairs of bricks in that column which also appear adjacent in the final pile.

(b) The number of adjacent pairs of bricks that make a correct pair but the wrong way up.

So:

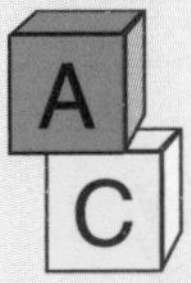

would score one in the 'Correct' row if the final heap had an A directly above a C and a one in the 'Reversed' row if the final heap had a C on top of an A. From all this, can you create the final pile before it topples?

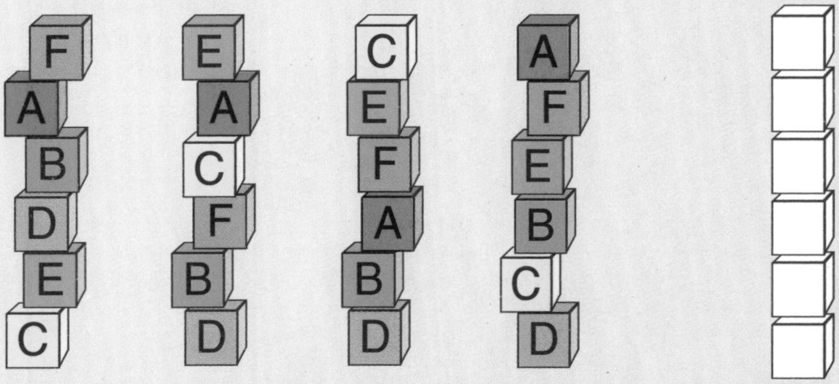

Correct	0	0	1	2	5
Reversed	0	1	0	1	0

35 BATTLESHIPS ★★

Do you remember the old game of battleships? These puzzles are based on that idea. Your task is to find the vessels in the diagram. Some parts of boats or sea squares have already been filled in, and a number next to a row or column refers to the number of occupied squares in that row or column. The boats may be positioned horizontally or vertically, but no two boats or parts of boats are in adjacent squares – horizontally, vertically or diagonally.

Aircraft carrier:

Battleships:

Cruisers: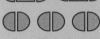

Destroyers:

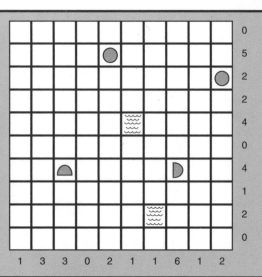

36 THE INVISIBLES ★

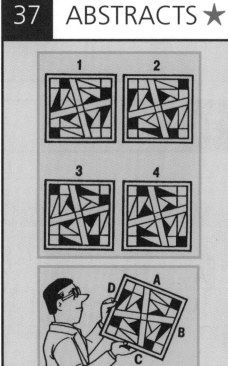

Many of the people in this circus scene are plainly visible. However, there are several more whose presence can only be inferred from various details in the picture. Can you expose the 'missing persons'?

37 ABSTRACTS ★

Geoff has bought one of the four abstract paintings shown at the top, but he can't remember which one it is or which way up it should go. Can you help him?

38 TSUNAMI ★★★

The numbers alongside each row or column tell you how many blocks of black squares are in a line. For example: 2, 3, 5 tells you that from left to right (or top to bottom) there is a group of two black squares, then at least one white space, then a group of three black squares, then at least one white shape, then a group of five black squares. Each block of black squares on the same line must have at least one white square between it and the next block of black squares.

Sometimes it is possible to tell which squares are going to be black without reference to other lines or columns. In the example below, we can deduce that any block of six black squares must incorporate the two central squares:

6

Can you complete this tsunami puzzle, to reveal the hidden pattern or picture?

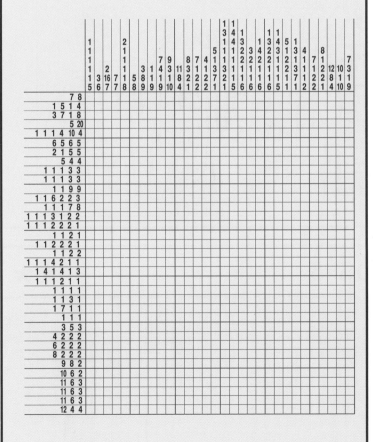

39 FINE LINES ★

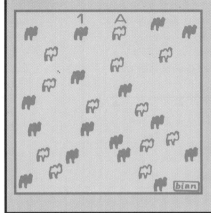

With one continuous line, join all the black camels (starting from number 1); with another continuous line, join all the white camels (starting from letter A). The lines must not cross!

40 DOMINO SEARCH ★★

A standard set of dominoes has been laid out, using numbers instead of dots for clarity. Using a sharp pencil and a keen brain, can you draw in the lines to show where each domino has been placed? You may find the check grid useful – crossing off each domino as you find it.

2	6	1	4	4	3	0	3
2	3	5	5	6	6	4	2
0	1	0	2	1	1	1	4
5	3	0	0	5	3	0	5
0	6	1	2	1	6	4	1
4	3	3	4	0	5	5	6
2	4	6	3	2	2	6	5

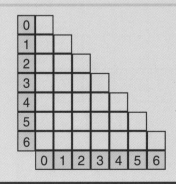

41   STAR LINES ★

With one continuous line, join up all the circles (starting from Pisces) and, with another continuous line, join up all the triangles (starting from Gemini). The lines must not cross!

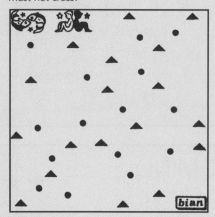

42   FIND THE FAKES   ★

The proud owners of the famous artist's paintiing (shown on top) are showing off their new acquisitions (shown below). Unfortunately, however, five of these are not the artist's original work, but are clever fakes. Which are the five fakes and how can you identify them?

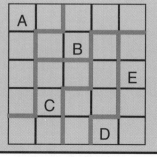

43   ABC   ★★

Each line, across and down, is to have each of the letters A, B and C, and two empty squares. The letter outside the grid shows the first or second letter in the direction of the arrow. Can you fill in the grid?

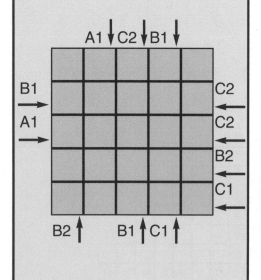

44   LOGI-5   ★★

Each line, across and down, is to have each of the letters A, B, C, D and E, appearing once each. Also, every shape – shown by the thick lines – must also have each of the letters in it. Can you fill in the grid?

45 MATCH THE HALVES ★★

These soldiers are all mixed up! Can you match the halves?

46 BIG TOP ★★

Karl Krack, who owns a small travelling circus, believes that variety is the spice of life and for each show he alters the order of his eight acts. Can you work out what the order will be for tonight's performance?

1	2	3	4
5	6	7	8

Fred the Fire-eater is two acts after the Flying Fortresses and three acts before the Agilles Acrobats. Senor Pedro's Poodles are three acts before the Crazy Carvellos but after Madame Poll's Parrots who are not starting the programme. The Clever Clowns are three acts before Jim the Juggler but they are after Senor Pedro's Poodles.

47 NUMBER JIG ★★

Fit the numbers into the grid as quickly as possible. We have given you some help.

3 figures	4 figures		
120	2512	16163	89233
122	8300	27891	90407
125	8328	30094	92248
253	8476	30627	96271
254		40111	
281	5 figures	40491	6 figures
283	10863	41138	250153
325	10875	42710	251155
326	11241	43336	471206
400	12248	43868	638471
527	12841	43939	738262
583	12845	73093	
800	14682	78865	
928	15572	79941	
		83544	

48 BALANCING THE SCALES ★★

How many stars are needed to balance scale C?

49 TRIPLETS ★

Which three of the waiters are carrying identical buckets?

50 TSUNAMI ★★★

The numbers alongside each row or column tell you how many blocks of black squares are in a line. For example: 2, 3, 5 tells you that from left to right (or top to bottom) there is a group of two black squares, then at least one white space, then a group of three black squares, then at least one white shape, then a group of five black squares. Each block of black squares on the same line must have at least one white square between it and the next block of black squares.

Sometimes it is possible to tell which squares are going to be black without reference to other lines or columns. In the example below, we can deduce that any block of six

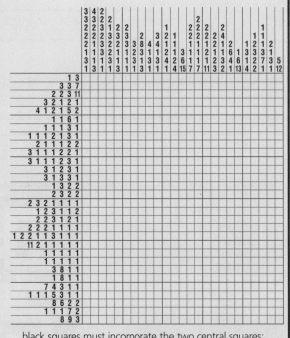

black squares must incorporate the two central squares:

6 ▢▢▢▢■▢▢▢▢

Can you complete this tsunami puzzle, to reveal the hidden pattern or picture?

51 COG-ITATE ★

Which point will be touched when the engineer turns the handle as shown?

52 WHO'S WHO? ★

Match up the pairs of brothers using the information given.

53 DROP-OUT ★

The collector is trying to select a snail. In the bottom picture, he has made his choice. Which snail did he choose?

54 LOGI-PATH ★★

Use your deductive reasoning to form a pathway from the box marked START to the box marked FINISH moving in either direction horizontally or vertically (but not diagonally). The number at the beginning of every row or column indicates exactly how many boxes in that row or column your pathway must pass through. The small diagram is given as an example of how it works.

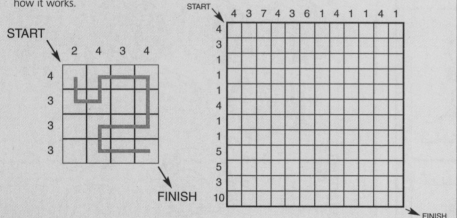

55 TSUNAMI ★★

The numbers alongside each row or column tell you how many blocks of black squares are in a line. For example: 2, 3, 5 tells you that from left to right (or top to bottom) there is a group of two black squares, then at least one white space, then a group of three black squares, then at least one white shape, then a group of five black squares. Each block of black squares on the same line must have at least one white square between it and the next block of black squares.

Sometimes it is possible to tell which squares are going to be black without reference to other lines or columns. In the example below, we can deduce that any block of six black squares must incorporate the two central squares:

6

Can you complete this tsunami puzzle, to reveal the hidden pattern or picture?

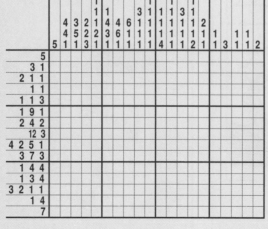

56 DOMINO SEARCH ★★

A standard set of dominoes has been laid out, using numbers instead of dots for clarity. Using a sharp pencil and a keen brain, can you draw in the lines to show where each domino has been placed? You may find the check grid useful – crossing off each domino as you find it.

57 LOGI-5 ★★

Each line, across and down, is to have each of the letters A, B, C, D and E, appearing once each. Also, every shape – shown by the thick lines – must also have each of the letters in it. Can you fill in the grid?

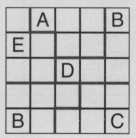

58 SAFE BET ★★

This is an odd type of safe. If you solve all the clues and enter them in the grid, the correct combination will appear in the shaded squares.

ACROSS
1   Add 220 to *4 across*
4   Multiply *21 down* by 4
6   Multiply *23 across* by 10
7   Subtract 200 from *1 across*
9   Add 4 to *1 across*
13 Add 666,581,666 to *6 across*
17 Half of *13 across*
20 Subtract 6,238 from *23 across*
23 5 per cent of 170,000
24 Add 36,262 to *12 down*

25 Subtract 1 from *26 across*
26 Next in series 715, 814, 913,...

DOWN
1   Multiply *4 down* by 10
2   Square 22
3   Add 100 to *4 down*
4   First three digits of *26 across*
5   Add 4,404 to *2 down*
8   Subtract 4,999 from *10 down*
10 Multiply 5 by 433,277

11 Add 26,033 to *23 down*
12 Subtract 10,096 from *11 down*
14 Add 60 to *15 down*
15 Square root of 375,769
16 Second, third and fourth digits of *11 down*
18 Add 199 to *26 across*
19 Add 991 to *25 across*
21 Subtract 357 from *22 down*
22 Square root of 369,664
23 Add 193 to *22 down*

59 WALKIES ★

Each picture is missing a detail that is present in the other seven. Can you spot all eight missing details?

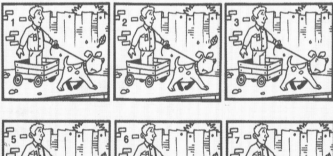

60 MISSING VALUES ★★

The numbers in each hexagon add up to the same total. Can you work out what that is, by finding the correct value for each symbol?

61   SAFE BET

This is an odd type of safe. If you solve all the clues and enter them in the grid, the correct combination will appear in the shaded squares.

ACROSS

1 Add *5 across* to *32 across*
3 Subtract 765 from *1 across*
5 First three digits of *26 down*
7 Divide *31 across* by 3
8 Multiply *7 across* by 59
9 Add 4 to *4 down*
11 Divide *17 down* by *7 across*
13 Multiply *18 down* by 5
14 3 per cent of 646,700
16 Square *1 across*
21 Square *34 across*
22 5 per cent of 1,026,100
25 Square root of 40,401
27 Divide *6 down* by *7 across*
28 Subtract *31 across* from

13 across
30 First three digits of *10 down*
31 First two digits of *24 down*
32 Add 692 to *33 across*
33 Divide *32 across* by 5
34 Subtract 103 from *1 across*

DOWN

1 Add *7 across* to *15 down*
2 Subtract 7,457,863 from *10 down*
4 Twice *5 across*
5 Multiply *1 across* by 2
6 Roman MM
9 Subtract 5,925,600 from *10 down*

10 Add 8,159,550 to *15 down*
12 First four digits of *2 down*
15 Multiply half of *7 across* by 1,981
17 Subtract 45 from *12 down*
18 Square root of 12,321
19 Multiply *34 across* by 3
20 Add 859,856 to *19 down*
23 Months in ninety-and-a-half years
24 Divide *31 across* by 2, then multiply by *25 across*
26 Multiply the first two digits of *4 down* by 51
29 Add 6 to *25 across*

62   TSUNAMI   ★★★

The numbers alongside each row or column tell you how many blocks of black squares are in a line. For example: 2, 3, 5 tells you that from left to right (or top to bottom) there is a group of two black squares, then at least one white space, then a group of three black squares, then at least one white shape, then a group of five black squares. Each block of black squares on the same line must have at least one white square between it and the next block of black squares.

Sometimes it is possible to tell which squares are going to be black without reference to other lines or columns. In the example below, we can deduce that any block of six black squares must incorporate the two central squares:

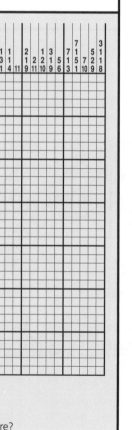

6 ▢▢▢▢▢■▢▢▢▢

Can you complete this tsunami puzzle, to reveal the hidden pattern or picture?

63   EASY AS ABC   ★★

Each row and column originally contained one A, one B, one C, one D and two blank squares. Each letter and number refer to the first or second of the four letters encountered when travelling in the direction of the arrow. Can you complete the original grid?

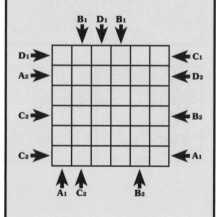

64 TSUNAMI ★★

The numbers alongside each row or column tell you how many blocks of black squares are in a line. For example: 2, 3, 5 tells you that from left to right (or top to bottom) there is a group of two black squares, then at least one white space, then a group of three black squares, then at least one white shape, then a group of five black squares. Each block of black squares on the same line must have at least one white square between it and the next block of black squares.

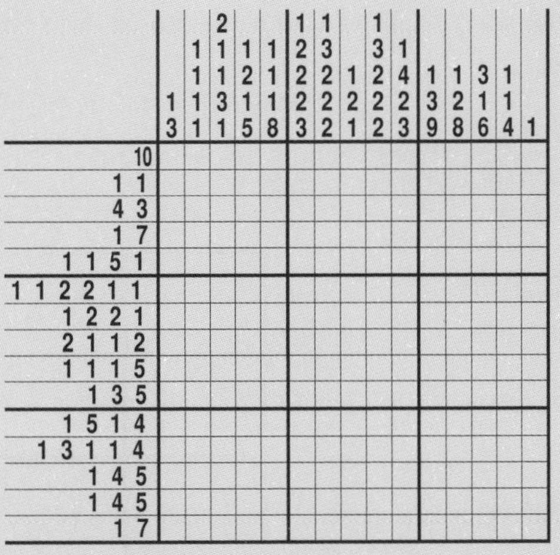
1 3
1 1 1 1
2 1 1 3 1
1 2 1 5
1 1 1 8
1 2 2 2 3
1 3 2 2 2
1 2 1
1 3 2 2 2
1 4 2 3
1 3 9
1 2 8
3 1 6
1 1 4
1
10
1 1
4 3
1 7
1 1 5 1
1 1 2 2 1 1
1 2 2 1
2 1 1 2
1 1 1 5
1 3 5
1 5 1 4
1 3 1 1 4
1 4 5
1 4 5
1 7

Sometimes it is possible to tell which squares are going to be black without reference to other lines or columns. In the example below, we can deduce that any block of six black squares must incorporate the two central squares:

6 

Can you complete this tsunami puzzle, to reveal the hidden pattern or picture?

65 TOGA PARTY ★

Each picture contains a detail that is not in the other three. Can you spot the four extra details?

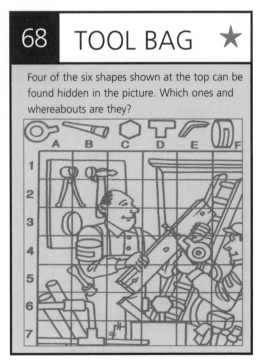

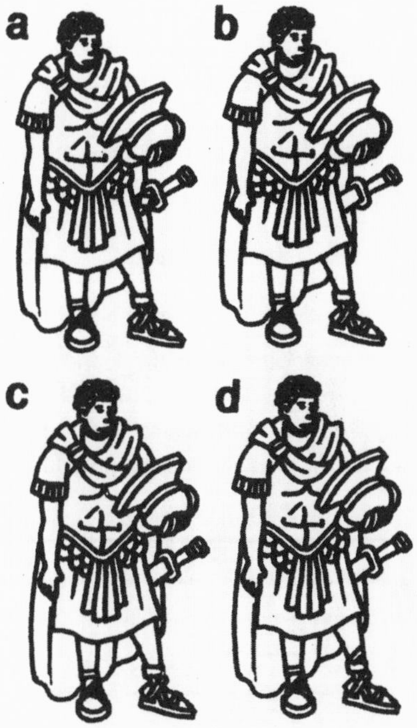
a
b
c
d

66 FOURSOME ★

Which four of the twelve vases are identical?

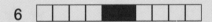

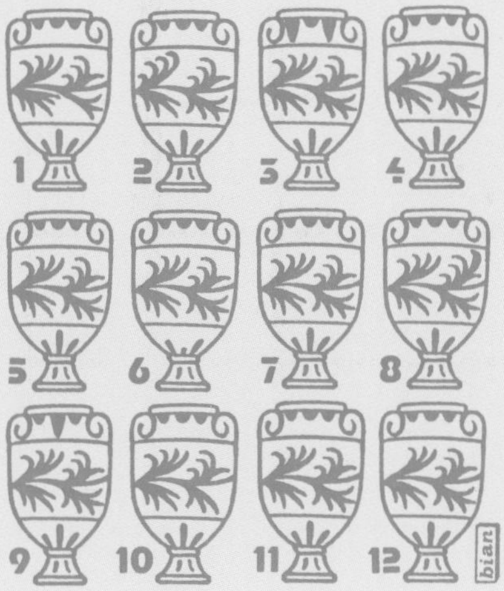
1
2
3
4
5
6
7
8
9
10
11
12

67 LINE UP ★

With one line, join all the white bowls (starting from number 1 and with straight lines from bowl to bowl); and with another, join all the black bowls (starting from A). The lines must not cross!

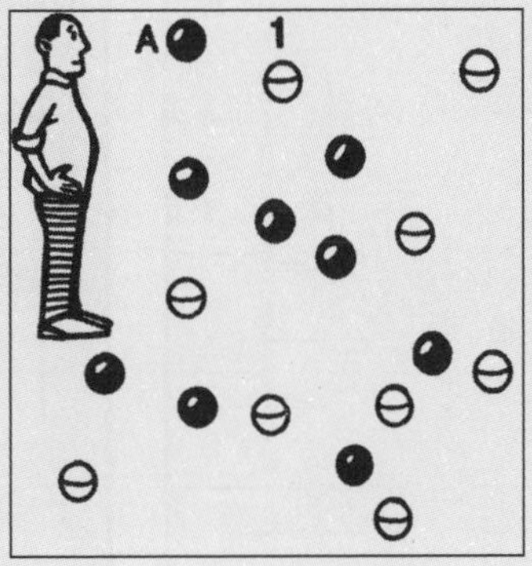
A
1

68 TOOL BAG ★

Four of the six shapes shown at the top can be found hidden in the picture. Which ones and whereabouts are they?

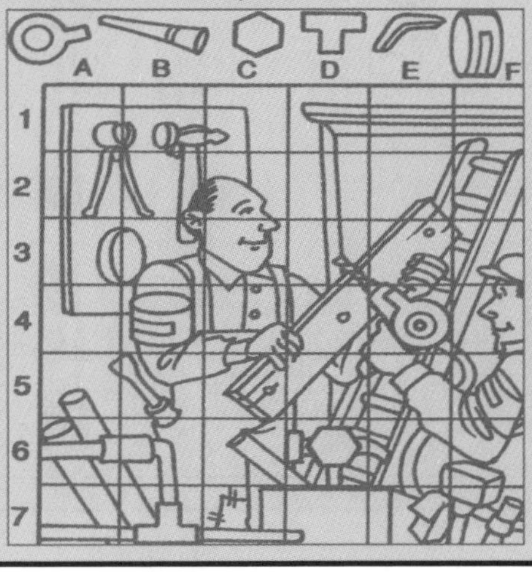
A
B
C
D
E
F
1
2
3
4
5
6
7

69 DAILY DOZEN

Here's a gentle mental exercise. Each of the twelve squares contains a different one of the numbers 1 to 12. From the clues given below, can you place them correctly?

Numbers: 1; 2; 3; 4; 5; 6; 7; 8; 9; 10; 11; 12

Clues

1 The 12 is in square B2; the numbers immediately to its left and diagonally below it to the left are both factors of it, one being an odd number.

2 The 6 is adjacent to the 10 in the same row, and is to be found in the same vertical column as the 8.

3 The numbers in squares A1 and C3, added together, give the one in square C4.

4 The 7 is immediately below the 4, and immediately to the right of the 5.

5 Neither the 2 nor the 1 is in column 1, though the 2 is in a column further left than the one containing the 11.

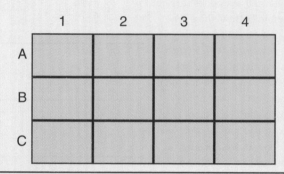

NB The numbers which are proper factors of 12 are 2, 3, 4 and 6.

Starting tip: First place the numbers referred to in clue 1.

70 PILE UP ★★

These piles of bricks aren't the random results of a child's play but clues to a final, at present blank, pile on the right. Like the rest, that one has six bricks each with a different one of the six letters. The numbers below the heaps tell you two things:

(a) The number of adjacent pairs of bricks in that column which also appear adjacent in the final pile.

(b) The number of adjacent pairs of bricks that make a correct pair but the wrong way up.

So: would score one in the 'Correct' row if the final heap had an A directly above a C and a one in the 'Reversed' row if the final heap had a C on top of an A. From all this, can you create the final pile before it topples?

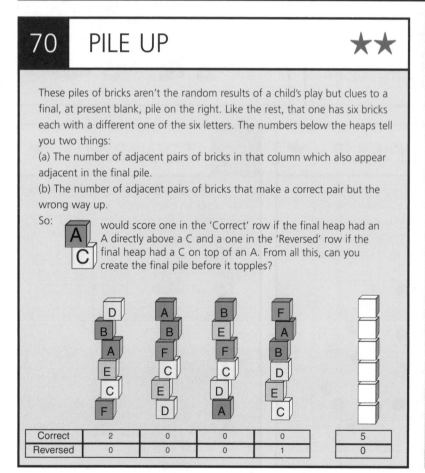

Correct	2	0	0	0		5
Reversed	0	0	0	1		0

71 LOGI-5 ★★

Each line, across and down, is to have each of the letters A, B, C, D and E, appearing once each. Also, every shape – shown by the thick lines, must also have each of the letters in it. Can you fill in the grid?

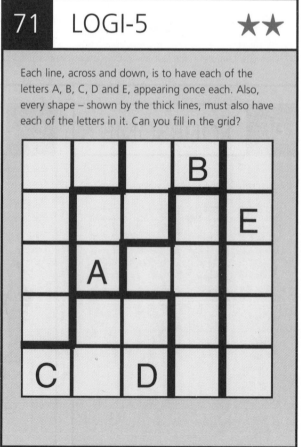

72 BATTLESHIPS

Do you remember the old game of battleships? These puzzles are based on that idea. Your task is to find the vessels in the diagram. Some parts of boats or sea squares have already been filled in, and a number next to a row or column refers to the number of occupied squares in that row or column. The boats may be positioned horizontally or vertically, but no two boats or parts of boats are in adjacent squares – horizontally, vertically or diagonally.

Aircraft-carrier:

Battleships:

Cruisers:

Destroyers:

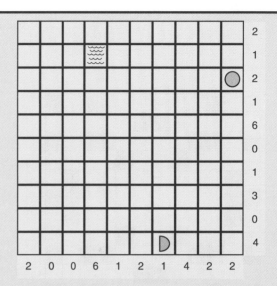

73 UP STICKS ★

In this puzzle, you have to imagine picking up each one of these six brooms in turn, but you can only pick the top one each time. In what order must you choose them?

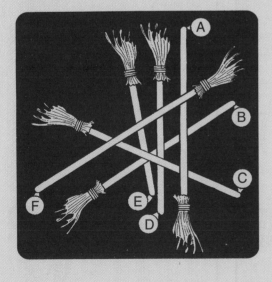

74 NUMBER SQUARES ★★

Can you place the numbers into the empty squares and make each equation (across and down) correct? Some are already in place.
The missing numbers are: 2, 3, 4, 5, 6, 7 , 7, 8, 9, 13 and 35.

75   SAFE BET

This is an odd type of safe. If you solve all the clues and enter them in the grid, the correct combination will appear in the shaded squares.

ACROSS

2   Square 789
7   Multiply 258 by 87, add 6,316
8   Divide 996,366 by 14
9   Add 789 to 987, subtract 64
12   Cube 18, subtract 735
15   Septuagenarian minimum age
16   Ounces in 77 pounds
19   Subtract 1,234,567 from 33,197,828
23   Cube 213, multiply by 10
25   Multiply 97 by 79, subtract 515
27   Not quite a century
28   Divide 397,600 by 56, add 111
30   Add twenty per cent of 3,185 to twenty-five per cent of 2,584
32   Yards in sixteen-and-a-half miles
34   Add 37,216 to 51,030
36   Subtract *2 across* from 1,221,393

DOWN

1   Square yards in an acre
2   Subtract one-ninth of 693 from143
3   Twelve-and-a-half per cent of 1,768
4   Multiply P's alphabetical position by Q's
5   Just shy of a dozen
6   Divide 264,627 by *27 across*
10   Cube 198
11   Add 266,166 to 765,432
12   Treble *22 down*
13   Add one-fifth of 226,645 to one-seventh of 335,755
14   Quadruple 17,792
16   Divide 22,194,844 by thirty-five per cent of 3,920
17   Multiply 237 by 85, add 1,157
18   Subtract the square of 14 from the cube of 6

20   Divide 20,152 by 22
21   Multiply 25 by 23, subtract 276
22   Square root of 289
24   Square root of 144
26   Add 873 to 1,125
29   Date of Dunkirk evacuation
30   Subtract one-third of 1,116 from a quarter of 1,924
31   Square 19, add 26
33   Subtract half-a-dozen from *12 down*
35   Hours in 295,200 seconds

76   MAZE-WAYS ★

Each obstacle along the path carries a penalty as shown in the key in the middle. Can you travel from A to B while incurring a total of 40 penalty points?

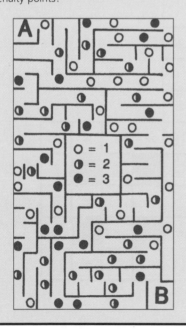

77   BLOCKS AWAY ★

The professor has discovered that there will be three blocks missing if he tries to reconstruct the orignal mural shown. Which ones are they?

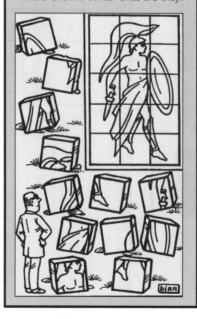

78   COG-ITATE ★

Which of the four weights will rise and which will fall when the handle is turned as shown?

79   TSUNAMI   ★★★

The numbers alongside each row or column tell you how many blocks of black squares are in a line. For example: 2, 3, 5 tells you that from left to right (or top to bottom) there is a group of two black squares, then at least one white space, then a group of three black squares, then at least one white shape, then a group of five black squares. Each block of black squares on the same line must have at least one white square between it and the next block of black squares.

Sometimes it is possible to tell which squares are going to be black without reference to other lines or columns. In the example below, we can deduce that any block of six black squares must incorporate the two central squares:

6

Can you complete this tsunami puzzle, to reveal the hidden pattern or picture?

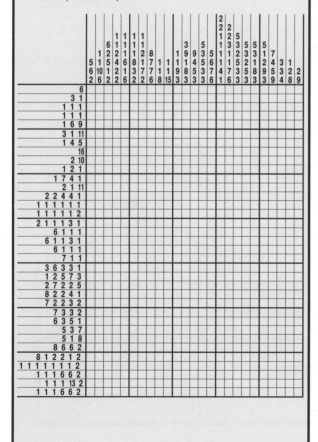

80   SNAP IT UP   ★

Which of the nine snapshots is the actual result of the picture taken by the photographer at the bottom?

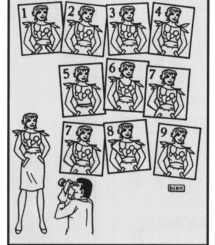

81   TREASURE HUNT   ★

The small piece of the map at the top shows under which large bush the treasure is buried. Can you work out in which square this is on the larger map?

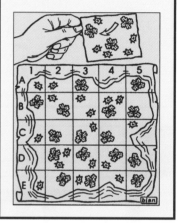

82   CRIME TIME   ★

Despite their hidden faces, the criminals involved in the four scenes at the top were soon arrested by a smart detective who identified them from other details. Can you spot the clues?

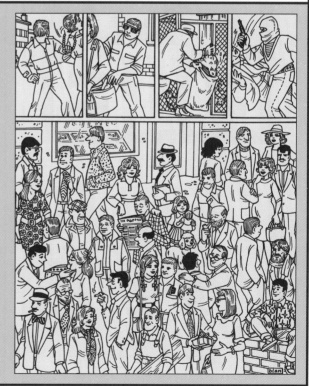

83 OFF FORM ★

Which one of the eight numbered pieces is the one which is missing from the broken bench?

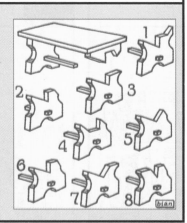

84 A BRIDGE TOO FAR ★★★

Eight men and eight women are playing bridge at four tables, as shown. At the game in hand, dummy is in a different position at each table, and the contract at each is in a different suit and for a different number of tricks – this number also differs in each case from the table number. With the following clues, can you position each person, and also say who is dummy and name the contract being played at each table?

Roger (South) is dummy on his table, which is numbered one lower than Connie's and one higher than Harry's, both of whom are in a different position from Roger and from each other, neither being dummy. Fred and Gordon are partners on the remaining table, neither being dummy. Alan (West) is on a table where the contract is 4 Spades. Tessa (dummy) is one table anti-clockwise from Eddie, at whose table the contract is for one trick more than on table 1.

Dummy on table 4 is the person whose name comes first alphabetically on that table. Jane and Dot are in the same position at different tables whose numbers are two apart; this is also true of Kate and Lola, the first-named in each case being at the lower-numbered table. From his seat Peter, who is not on table 2, can see table 2, but not table 4; his contract is in Diamonds, while Michael's table is going for Hearts, but one fewer.

Susie (dummy) has Jane on her left and Harry on her right; her partner is Peter, and the contract is for one more than the table number. Connie has Dot on her left, who is not in the same position as Fred. Tessa, whose table is playing a red-suit contract, is in the same relative position as Babs.

85 NUMBER JIG ★★

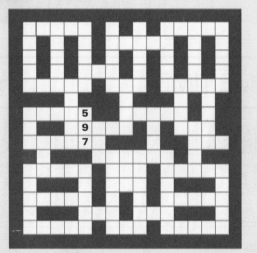

Fit the numbers into the grid as quickly as possible. One has been done for you.

3 figures	4 figures		
182	3294	28398	92108
189	5662	39264	92316
192	7353	47028	98184
219	8326	47119	99215
238		50264	
304	5 figures	51329	6 figures
381	13802	60138	327453
410	17608	63258	518007
560	17974	70910	613254
565	19344	80809	810871
597	23509	81101	951326
763	23916	86065	
835	24415	87552	
897	26231	90804	
		91505	

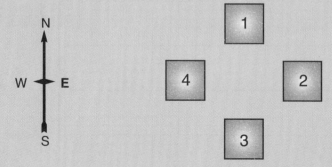

	Table 1	Table 2	Table 3	Table 4
N				
E				
S				
W				
Contract				

86 LOGI-PATH

Use your deductive reasoning to form a pathway from the box marked START to the box marked FINISH moving in either direction horizontally or vertically (but not diagonally). The number at the beginning of every row or column indicates exactly how many boxes in that row or column your pathway must pass through. The small diagram is given as an example of how it works.

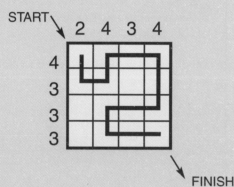

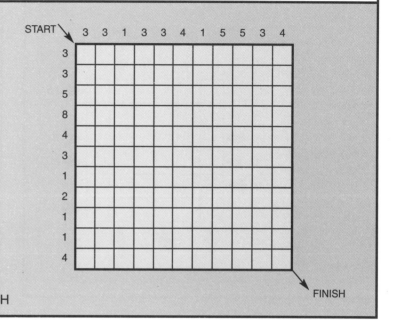

87 TSUNAMI ★★★

The numbers alongside each row or column tell you how many blocks of black squares are in a line. For example: 2, 3, 5 tells you that from left to right (or top to bottom) there is a group of two black squares, then at least one white space, then a group of three black squares, then at least one white shape, then a group of five black squares. Each block of black squares on the same line must have at least one white square between it and the next block of black squares.

Sometimes it is possible to tell which squares are going to be black without reference to other lines or columns. In the example below, we can deduce that any block of six black squares must incorporate the two central squares:

Can you complete this tsunami puzzle, to reveal the hidden pattern or picture?

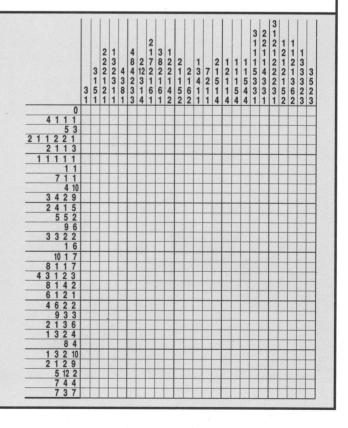

88 EASY AS ABC ★★

Each row and column originally contained one A, one B, one C, one D and two blank squares. Each letter and number refer to the first or second of the four letters encountered when travelling in the direction of the arrow. Can you complete the original grid?

Clues around the grid:

Top: C₁ B₁ A₂ A₂
Right: D₁, B₂, D₁, A₂
Left: A₂, B₁, D₂
Bottom: B₁ C₂ D₂

89 TSUNAMI ★★★

The numbers alongside each row or column tell you how many blocks of black squares are in a line. For example: 2, 3, 5 tells you that from left to right (or top to bottom) there is a group of two black squares, then at least one white space, then a group of three black squares, then at least one white shape, then a group of five black squares. Each block of black squares on the same line must have at least one white square between it and the next block of black squares.

Sometimes it is possible to tell which squares are going to be black without reference to other lines or columns. In the example below, we can deduce that any block of six black squares must incorporate the two central squares:

6 ☐☐☐☐■■☐☐☐☐

Can you complete this tsunami puzzle, to reveal the hidden pattern or picture?

Row clues (top to bottom):
- 11 4
- 5 4 8
- 2 1 1 1 10
- 1 1 4 2 7
- 2 2 1 1 2 4
- 5 4 1 1 1
- 3 7 1 1 1
- 3 6 1 2 2
- 3 4 1 1 1 1
- 3 5 1 1
- 4 6 1 2 1
- 6 7 1 4 1
- 6 11 2
- 7 8 4 2
- 9 6 2
- 4 1 4 3 2 3
- 1 1 1 1 10 3
- 1 2 4 4 1 4
- 1 3 1 1 3 1 5
- 6 4 3 3
- 11 3 7
- 1 3 8
- 1 2 2 2 3
- 12 2 9
- 2 2 2 3

90 WRAPPED UP ★

Which of the four numbered cubes is identical to the one held by the boy?

91 SAFE BET

This is an odd type of safe. If you solve all the clues and enter them in the grid, the correct combination will appear in the shaded squares.

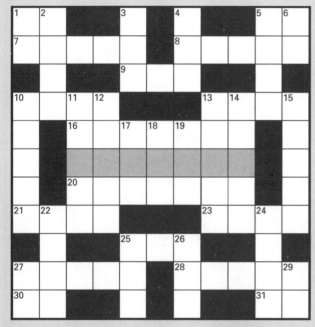

ACROSS

1 Square root of *4 down*
5 Square root of 1,936
7 Add 12,178 to *8 across*
8 Ounces in 1,253 pounds
9 Add 900 to *1 across*
10 Twice *23 across*
13 Add 1,000 to *22 down*
16 Square *2 down*
20 Square *24 down*
21 Divide *29 down* by 3, then
      multiply by 1,051
23 Add 1,881 to *26 down*
25 Next in series 95, 104, 113, …
27 Last five digits of *20 across*
28 Subtract 4,080 from *15 down*
30 Subtract 20 from *5 across*
31 Multiply *1 across* by 5

DOWN

1 Square root of *3 down*

2 Subtract 40,193 from *11 down*
3 Square root of 28,561
4 Subtract 1 from *25 across*
5 First four digits of *10 down*
6 Twice *30 across*
10 Multiply *29 down* by 2,967
11 Multiply *29 down* by 2,763
12 Subtract 16,250 from *11 down*
13 Subtract 24,229 from *14 down*
14 Add 4,126 to *27 across*
15 Subtract 4 from *10 down*
17 Square last two digits of *27 across*
18 Square root of 504,100
19 Subtract three times *1 down*
      from *17 down*
22 Twice *2 down*
24 Half of *5 down*
25 Multiply *29 down* by 10
26 Multiply *30 across* by 10
27 First two digits of *21 across*
29 Square root of 225

---

92 IN THE ABSTRACT ★

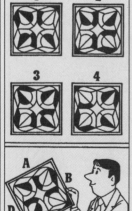

On the left are four abstract paintings hanging in a famous gallery. The man shown has bought one, but he can't remember which one, or which way up it should go. Can you help him?

---

93 HARP ON ★

Four of the harp-players have mirror images. Which are the four pairs and which is the odd-one-out?

---

94 POT LUCK ★

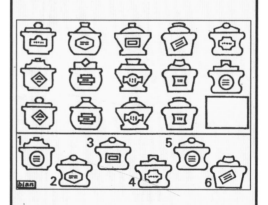

Which of the numbered pots should logically occupy the empty square?

95   NUMBERS UP   ★

Can you discover the logical sequence shown here and work out what number should replace the question-mark?

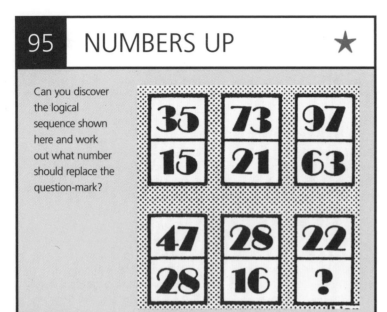

96   THAT LITTLE BIT OF DIFFERENCE   ★

There are eight differences between the two cartoons. Can you spot them?

97   DROP OUT   ★

The man is trying to buy a scarf. In the bottom picture he's made his choice. Which one did he buy?

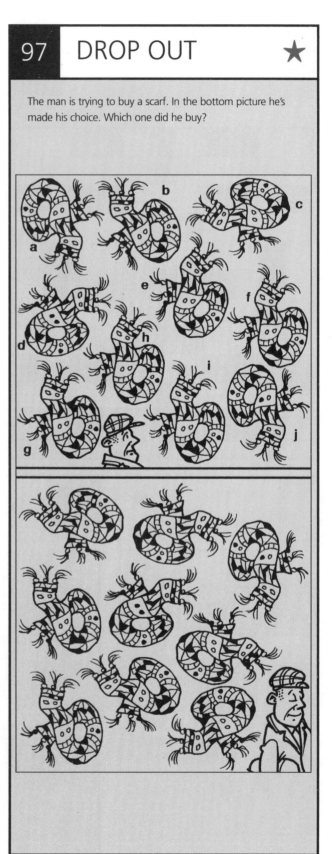

98 CIRCLE OF DIGITS ★★★

The figure below consists of three concentric circles divided into eight sectors; the three single-figure numbers in each sector add up to 15. The circles will be referred to as outer, middle and inner and one number in the inner has been inserted to give you a start. From the clues given, can you insert all the other numbers?

Clues
1   The only 0 appears in the outer circle, where there is no 1 or 3; there is no 9 in the middle and no number is repeated in any sector or circle.
2   All the numbers in sectors A and B are odd; B outer is one more than C inner and one less than H middle, which is one more than H inner; B inner is one less than G outer.
3   The 6 in the outer circle is diagonally opposite the 6 in the inner.
4   C inner is double D inner, while D outer is double D middle; F outer is double F middle, which is double G middle and the same as C outer; E outer is the same as A middle.

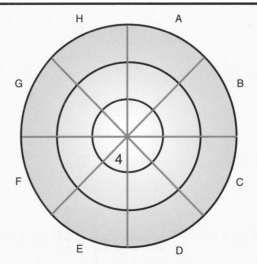

Starting tip: Work out the number in C inner.

99 PILE UP ★★

These piles of bricks aren't the random results of a child's play but clues to a final, at present blank, pile on the right. Like the rest, that one has six bricks each with a different one of the six letters. The numbers below the heaps tell you two things:
(a) The number of adjacent pairs of bricks in that column which also appear adjacent in the final pile.
(b) The number of adjacent pairs of bricks that make a correct pair but the wrong way up.
So:

 would score one in the 'Correct' row if the final heap had an A directly above a C and a one in the 'Reversed' row if the final heap had a C on top of an A. From all this, can you create the final pile before it topples?

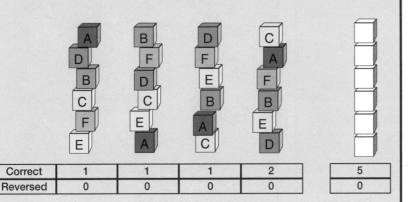

| Correct | 1 | 1 | 1 | 2 | | 5 |
| Reversed | 0 | 0 | 0 | 0 | | 0 |

100 LOGI-5 ★★

Each line, across and down, is to have each of the letters A, B, C, D and E, appearing once each. Also, every shape – shown by the thick lines – must also have each of the letters in it. Can you fill in the grid?

101 EASY AS ABC ★★

Each row and column originally contained one A, one B, one C, one D and two blank squares. Each letter and number refer to the first or second of the four letters encountered when travelling in the direction of the arrow. Can you complete the original grid?

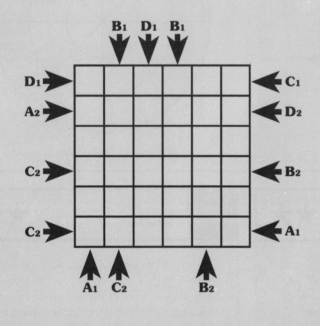

102 POUR TRICK ★★

A very old puzzle is still sometimes dragged out at parties or in pubs – especially as a means to win an easy bet. A full wine bottle is placed on the table. It has its cork in place and its unbroken plastic seal. The perpetrator of the plot then claims to be able to drink wine from the bottle – without removing the seal or the cork and without smashing the bottle. You now have two choices – win the bet by telling the trickster how it can be done or lose the bet and look up the answer.

104 BLACK OUT ★

Can you see which two dinosaurs are shown in silhouette at the top?

103 HOW FEW? ★★

What is the smallest group of people you can have that contains all these relationships?

aunt   brother   cousin   daughter   father

mother   nephew   niece   sister   son   uncle

105 MIRROR, MIRROR ★

Which three of the nine reversed images belong to Amy, Belinda and Cathy, shown at the top?

106 WHO'S WHO? ★

Can you match each cowboy to his son?

107 WOODWORK

Eight snaps have been taken of the large scene. However, only four of them were taken at exactly the same time. Which four are they?

108 TSUNAMI

The numbers alongside each row or column tell you how many blocks of black squares are in a line. For example: 2, 3, 5 tells you that from left to right (or top to bottom) there is a group of two black squares, then at least one white space, then a group of three black squares, then at least one white shape, then a group of five black squares. Each block of black squares on the same line must have at least one white square between it and the next block of black squares.

Sometimes it is possible to tell which squares are going to be black without reference to other lines or columns. In the example below, we can deduce that any block of six black squares must incorporate the two central squares:

6 ☐☐☐☐■■☐☐☐☐

Can you complete this tsunami puzzle, to reveal the hidden pattern or picture?

Column clues (left to right, read top to bottom):

Col	Clues
1	5
2	4 5
3	1 2 1
4	1 3 2 3
5	3 1 1 1 4
6	3 2 1 1 1 1 1
7	1 1 1 1 4 1
8	1 1 3 1 4 3 1
9	1 1 1 1 3 3 1
10	1 3 3 1 2 3 1
11	1 1 2 1 1 2 1
12	1 5 1 2 1
13	2 6 1
14	6 2
15	6 4 5
16	8 3
17	5 1 5
18	4 12
19	5 5
20	4

Row clues (top to bottom):

Row clues
13
4 6
1 2 2 5
2 1 2 6
3 1 4 6
4 3 1 3 1
2 2 4 1 2 1
1 1 1 1 1 1
2 3 1
1 1 1
1 3 1 1
1 4 1 1
8 1 1 1
1 1 1 1
10 1
1 7 1 3
1 4 1 1 4
1 1 2 6
1 3 7
1 8

109 DIVIDE THE SHAPES

Can you divide the picture below by drawing three straight lines to produce four sections, each containing nine different shapes?

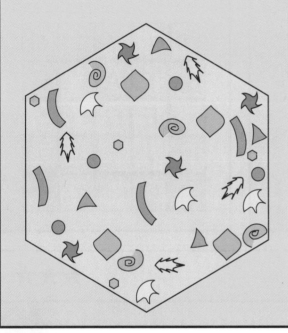

110 PILE UP

These piles of bricks aren't the random results of a child's play but clues to a final, at present blank, pile on the right. Like the rest, that one has six bricks each with a different one of the six letters. The numbers below the heaps tell you two things:

(a) The number of adjacent pairs of bricks in that column which also appear adjacent in the final pile.

(b) The number of adjacent pairs of bricks that make a correct pair but the wrong way up.

So:

 would score one in the 'Correct' row if the final heap had an A directly above a C and a one in the 'Reversed' row if the final heap had a C on top of an A. From all this, can you create the final pile before it topples?

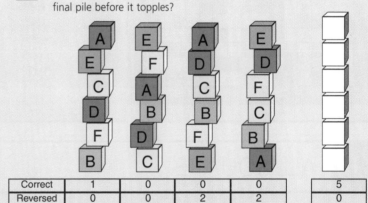

Correct	1	0	0	0	5
Reversed	0	0	2	2	0

111 BATTLESHIPS

Do you remember the old game of battleships? These puzzles are based on that idea. Your task is to find the vessels in the diagram. Some parts of boats or sea squares have already been filled in, and a number next to a row or column refers to the number of occupied squares in that row or column. The boats may be positioned horizontally or vertically, but no two boats or parts of boats are in adjacent squares – horizontally, vertically or diagonally.

Aircraft carrier:

Battleships:

Cruisers:

Destroyers:

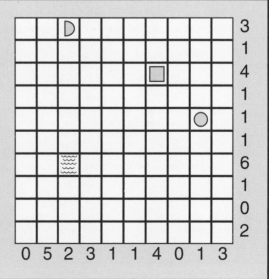

112 NUMBER JIG ★★

Fit the numbers into the grid as quickly as possible. One has been done for you.

3 figures	4882	6 figures
119	5215	106112
(238)	5907	125388
308	6899	231456
483	7606	254329
576	9814	371924
698		406138
801	5 figures	432901
993	13508	470719
	24134	523250
4 figures	29501	618383
1031	31886	634205
2801	54396	713248
3558	65908	893071
3560	89099	900102
3992		942603
4376		964131

113 LOGI-5 ★★

Each line, across and down, is to have each of the letters A, B, C, D and E, appearing once each. Also, every shape – shown by the thick lines – must also have each of the letters in it. Can you fill in the grid?

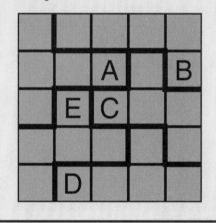

114 ALL SQUARE ★★★

A garden square in the city centre has a large hotel occupying each of its sides, as shown numbered 1 to 4 in the diagram. From the clues given below, can you name each hotel and its manager, and say how many rooms it boasts?

Clues

1 The hotel run by Max is directly across the square from the Majestic, which has more rooms, and which is not managed by Rupert.

2 The hotel on the western side of the square does not have 203 rooms.

3 The hotel with the fewest rooms occupies the north side of the square.

4 Guy runs the Castle Hotel, which is next anti-clockwise round the square from the one with 197 rooms.

5 Perry is the manager of the hotel numbered 3 on the plan, which has fewer rooms than the Excelsior.

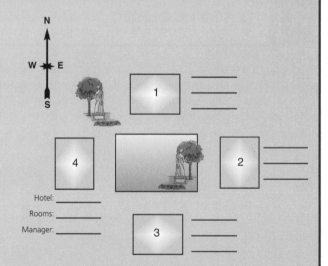

Hotel: _____
Rooms: _____
Manager: _____

Hotels: Castle; Excelsior; Grand; Majestic
Managers: Guy; Max; Perry; Rupert
Rooms: 158; 197; 203; 224

Starting tip: Begin by working out how many rooms there are in hotel 4.

115 TSUNAMI

The numbers alongside each row or column tell you how many blocks of black squares are in a line. For example: 2, 3, 5 tells you that from left to right (or top to bottom) there is a group of two black squares, then at least one white space, then a group of three black squares, then at least one white shape, then a group of five black squares. Each block of black squares on the same line must have at least one white square between it and the next block of black squares.

Sometimes it is possible to tell which squares are going to be black without reference to other lines or columns. In the example below, we can deduce that any block of six black squares must incorporate the two central squares:

6 ▢▢▢▢■▢▢▢▢

Can you complete this tsunami puzzle, to reveal the hidden pattern or picture?

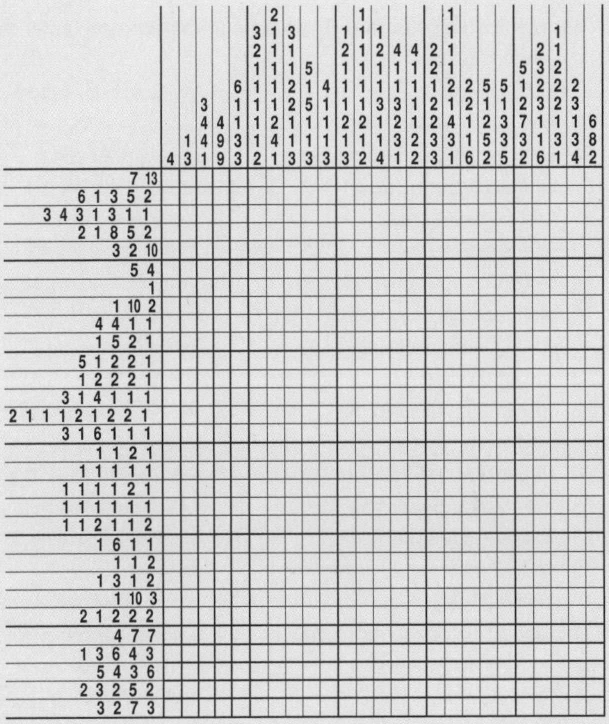

Row clues (top to bottom):
- 7 13
- 6 1 3 5 2
- 3 4 3 1 3 1 1
- 2 1 8 5 2
- 3 2 10
- 5 4
- 1
- 1 10 2
- 4 4 1 1
- 1 5 2 1
- 5 1 2 2 1
- 1 2 2 2 1
- 3 1 4 1 1 1
- 2 1 1 1 2 1 2 2 1
- 3 1 6 1 1 1
- 1 1 2 1
- 1 1 1 1 1
- 1 1 1 1 2 1
- 1 1 1 1 1 1
- 1 1 2 1 1 2
- 1 6 1 1
- 1 1 2
- 1 3 1 2
- 1 10 3
- 2 1 2 2 2
- 4 7 7
- 1 3 6 4 3
- 5 4 3 6
- 2 3 2 5 2
- 3 2 7 3

---

116 EASY AS ABC ★★

Each row and column originally contained one A, one B, one C, one D and two blank squares. Each letter and number refer to the first or second of the four letters encountered when travelling in the direction of the arrow. Can you complete the original grid?

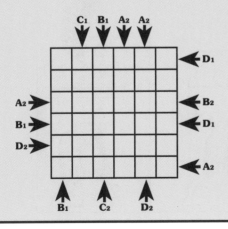

---

117 PASS ★★

There was an unusual result this year at Claggthorpe's Mastermind Competition – all four ended up with just 13 points each. After a quick call to Magnus, from the payphone in the lounge bar of the Battered Hen, it was announced that the contestant with the fewest number of passes would be the winner. Can you work out who that was?

1 The post-person who had specialized in Stone Age Poetry had one fewerpasses than Wendy Dee who is not the police officer.
2 Hugh Seddit had one more pass than the specialist in Soap Operas.
3 Watt Wazzit had specialized in the life and times of Bernard Gribble (his great-uncle) but he is not the barperson who had four passes.
4 The man who specialized in Bolton Brickworks of the late 18th century is not the shopkeeper who had one fewer passes than Ivor Started.

NAME	JOB	SUBJECT	PASSES
HUGH			
IVOR			
WATT			
WENDY			

118 SAFE BET

This is an odd type of safe. If you solve all the clues and enter them in the grid, the correct combination will appear in the shaded squares.

ACROSS

2 First four digits of *16 across*
6 Subtract 28 down from *6 down*
8 Subtract 1 from *1 down*
9 Add 61 to *34 across*
12 Add 3 to *2 across*
14 Multiply *6 across* by *33 down*
16 Multiply *12 across* by *33 down*, then subtract 23
18 Square *6 down*
22 3,992,004 multiplied by *5 down*
24 15 per cent of 613,700
25 Subtract 41, 546 from *24 across*
26 First four digits of *22 across*
29 Add *23 down* to *32 across*, then subtract 1,000
31 Subtract *33 down* from *1 down*
32 Add 117 to *2 across*
34 Twice *28 down*

DOWN

1 Square root of *34 across*
3 Square root of 110,889

4 Multiply *3 down* by 3
5 Divide *34 across* by the square of *33 down*
6 Square *1 down*, then add 7,285
7 Multiply *1 down* by 20,467,900
10 Subtract 189,171,485 from *7 down*
11 Divide *6 down* by 5
12 Multiply 16 by 68,241
13 Square *9 across*, then add 5,367,136
15 Add 25,975 to *17 down*
17 1,623 multiplied by a score
19 Multiply *1 down* by *33 down*, then add 7
20 Subtract 21 from *3 down*
21 Divide *23 down* by 4
23 Multiply *4 down* by 8
27 Add 3 to *3 down*
28 Multiply *1 down* by 20
30 Add 12 to *1 down*
33 Divide *1 down* by 4

119 WHO'S WHO?

Can you match each husband to his wife?

120 FUNNY FAKES ★

The proud owners of the famous artist's paintings (top) are showing off their new acquisitions (bottom). Unfortunately, however, five of these are not really the artist's original work but are clever fakes. Which are the fakes and how can you identify them?

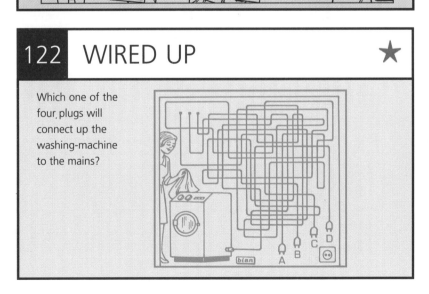

122 WIRED UP ★

Which one of the four plugs will connect up the washing-machine to the mains?

121 TRILINES ★

Can you draw three straight lines, each one drawn from one edge to another, so that they divide the box into five sections each containing a cup and a saucer?

123 IN THE SWIM ★

The three fishes shown at the top can be seen in silhouette. Which silhouette belongs to which fish?

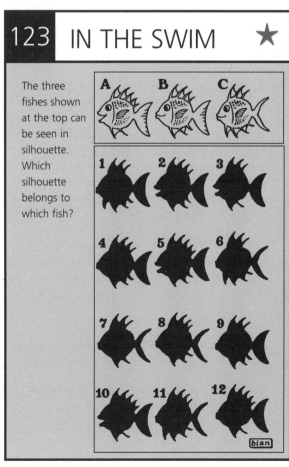

124 DROP-OUT ★

The man is trying to choose a briefcase. In the picture on the right, he has made his choice. Which briefcase did he choose?

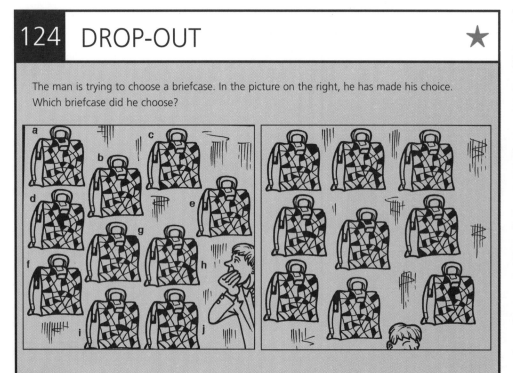

125 LOGI-5 ★★

Each line, across and down, is to have each of the letters A, B, C, D and E, appearing once each. Also, every shape – shown by the thick lines – must also have each of the letters in it. Can you fill in the grid?

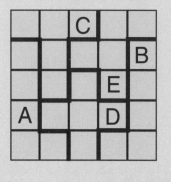

126 TSUNAMI ★★★

The numbers alongside each row or column tell you how many blocks of black squares are in a line. For example: 2, 3, 5 tells you that from left to right (or top to bottom) there is a group of two black squares, then at least one white space, then a group of three black squares, then at least one white shape, then a group of five black squares. Each block of black squares on the same line must have at least one white square between it and the next block of black squares.

Sometimes it is possible to tell which squares are going to be black without reference to other lines or columns. In the example below, we can deduce that any block of six black squares must incorporate the two central squares:

6

Can you complete this tsunami puzzle, to reveal the hidden pattern or picture?

Row clues:
- 2 9
- 1 1 5
- 4 5 5
- 2 2 3 5
- 2 1 1 1 2 1
- 2 1 1 2 1
- 2 1 1 4
- 2 2 2 1 4
- 2 3 1 3
- 2 1 3 1 1
- 1 1 5 2 2
- 6 8 4
- 1 1 7 6
- 6 7 6
- 1 1 3 1 8
- 6 6 4 3
- 2 2 3 1 3 2
- 1 2 1 6 3 1 2
- 1 2 1 6 3 2
- 14 4 3
- 2 7 4 8
- 1 1 1 3 1 6
- 1 3 1 3 1 6
- 2 2 2 2 2 4
- 3 3 6

127 PILE UP

These piles of bricks aren't the random results of a child's play but clues to a final, at present blank, pile on the right. Like the rest, that one has six bricks each with a different one of the six letters. The numbers below the heaps tell you two things:

(a) The number of adjacent pairs of bricks in that column which also appear adjacent in the final pile.

(b) The number of adjacent pairs of bricks that make a correct pair but the wrong way up.

So:

 would score one in the 'Correct' row if the final heap had an A directly above a C and a one in the 'Reversed' row if the final heap had a C on top of an A. From all this, can you create the final pile before it topples?

Correct	0	0	0	1	5
Reversed	1	2	1	0	0

128 STRAPPED ★★★

The six straps leading from the central hexagon each contain three different instances of the numbers 1 to 18. From the clues given below, can you place each number in the correct position on the correct strap?

Clues

1 The six innermost numbers total 64.

2 The single-digit middle number on strap A minus the number outside it produces the outermost number on strap F.

3 There are just two even numbers, one of which is the outermost one, on strap E, but only one on strap F.

4 5 is the innermost number on strap D; the 7 is not on the strap directly opposite.

5 17 and 12 are separated by the 1 on one of the straps.

6 The 10 on one strap, which is immediately next to the 16, is in the same relative position as the 3 on another, but the 6 is further away from the centre than the 15 on an adjacent strap.

7 Strap C, which has only one two-digit number on it, does not contain the 1 or 2, which corresponds in its position with the 13 on another strap.

8 The largest of the three numbers on strap B is not its innermost one; the outermost one is a lower number than the innermost number of the strap opposite, which is ten higher than the corresponding number on strap F.

Starting tip: Start by working out which is the strap referred to in clue 5.

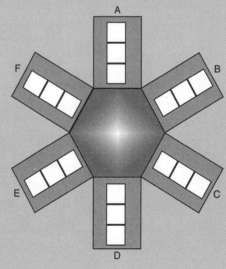

129 BATTLESHIPS

Do you remember the old game of battleships? These puzzles are based on that idea. Your task is to find the vessels in the diagram. Some parts of boats or sea squares have already been filled in, and a number next to a row or column refers to the number of occupied squares in that row or column. The boats may be positioned horizontally or vertically, but no two boats or parts of boats are in adjacent squares – horizontally, vertically or diagonally.

Aircraft carrier:

Battleships:

Cruisers:

Destroyers:

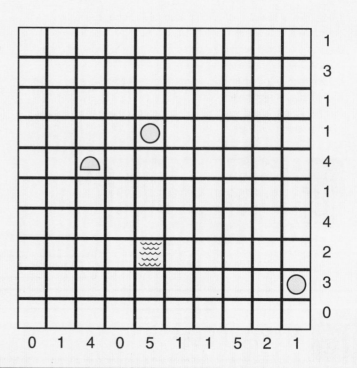

130 NUMBER JIG

Fit the numbers into the grid as quickly as possible. One has been done for you.

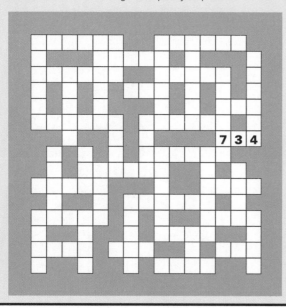

3 figures	6799	6 figures
193	6839	145637
285	7443	288016
556	8304	356174
586	9389	389077
638		421864
(734)	5 figures	478321
817	28946	508116
929	29280	512630
	40665	553681
4 figures	56833	603845
1064	57813	612349
1880	72353	745723
2586	89936	765381
3060		850337
4992		900964
5365		953341
5813		

131 LOGI-PATH ★★

Use your deductive reasoning to form a pathway from the box marked START to the box marked FINISH moving in either direction horizontally or vertically (but not diagonally). The number at the beginning of every row or column indicates exactly how many boxes in that row or column your pathway must pass through. The small diagram is given as an example of how it works.

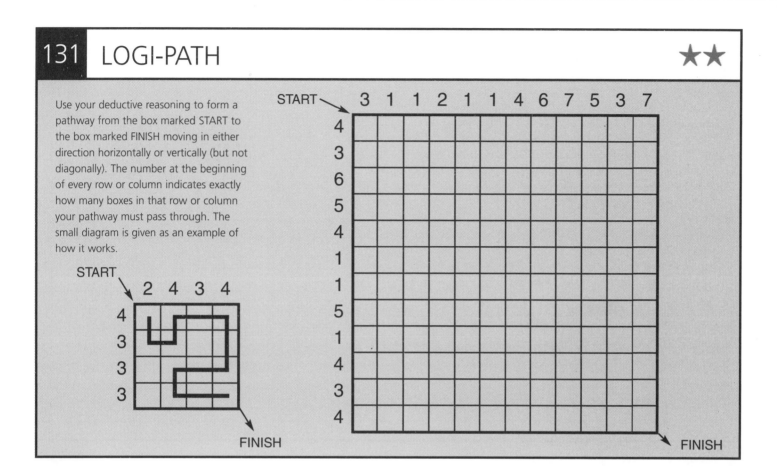

132 TSUNAMI ★★

The numbers alongside each row or column tell you how many blocks of black squares are in a line. For example: 2, 3, 5 tells you that from left to right (or top to bottom) there is a group of two black squares, then at least one white space, then a group of three black squares, then at least one white shape, then a group of five black squares. Each block of black squares on the same line must have at least one white square between it and the next block of black squares.

Sometimes it is possible to tell which squares are going to be black without reference to other lines or columns. In the example below, we can deduce that any block of six black squares must incorporate the two central squares:

6 ▢▢▢▢◼◼▢▢▢▢

Can you complete this tsunami puzzle, to reveal the hidden pattern or picture?

133   TSUNAMI

The numbers alongside each row or column tell you how many blocks of black squares are in a line. For example: 2, 3, 5 tells you that from left to right (or top to bottom) there is a group of two black squares, then at least one white space, then a group of three black squares, then at least one white shape, then a group of five black squares. Each block of black squares on the same line must have at least one white square between it and the next block of black squares.

Sometimes it is possible to tell which squares are going to be black without reference to other lines or columns. In the example below, we can deduce that any block of six black squares must incorporate the two central squares:

6   ☐☐☐☐■■☐☐☐☐

Can you complete this tsunami puzzle, to reveal the hidden pattern or picture?

Row clues:
- 13 10
- 13 8
- 1 10 3
- 1 11 2
- 1 15
- 1 3 3
- 1 2 9 2
- 1 2 1 1 1 2
- 1 4 1 1 1 4
- 1 1 11 1
- 1 1 1 1
- 1 1 2 1
- 1 1 1
- 1 1 2 1 1
- 1 2 5 2
- 3 1 1
- 1 1 5 3
- 3 1 1
- 13
- 3 4 4 3
- 3 9 3
- 4 4 4 4
- 5 8 5
- 2 3 3 3 2 2
- 3 2 7 3 2
- 3 3 2 2 3 2
- 3 2 5 3 2
- 3 3 2 2 4 2
- 1 2 3 5 4 3
- 2 2 3 2 2 4 2 1

134   SAFE BET   ★★

This is an odd type of safe. If you solve all the clues and enter them in the grid, the correct combination will appear in the shaded squares.

ACROSS

1   Subtract 2 from 24 squared
3   *8 across*, add 7
5   Square 23, add 6
7   Divide 657 by 9
8   Divide 10,465 by 13
9   Multiply *27 across* by 4, add 9
11   Multiply 78 by 3 squared
13   Emergency call number
14   Fifteen per cent of *21 across*, subtract 14
16   Square 546, add 8
21   Minutes in a leap year
22   Multiply 3,007 by 18
25   Two-thirds of 1,473, subtract 29
27   Add 66 to the square root of *1 down*
28   Blackbirds in the pie multiplied by 10
30   VII times XIX
31   Ali Baba plus his thieves
32   Ten times a baker's dozen
33   Two-thirds of 732
34   Square 11, multiply by 3, subtract from 1,143

DOWN

1   Square 29 down, divide by 36
2   Multiply 19,197 by 25
4   Multiply square root of 289 by 8
5   Three-fifths of 8,450
6   *26 down* plus 12 dozen
9   2,349,116 plus 3,133,146
10   31,817 multiply by 9 score
12   Divide 70,912 by 32, subtract 7
15   7,513 plus *19 down*
17   Add 5,792 to *26 down*
18   25 per cent of 468
19   Seoul falls to Communists
20   Subtract 323,492 from 932,709
23   Add 65 squared to 88
24   Pluto discovered
26   Multiply 96 by 35
29   One-eighth of *6 down*

135 DARTING ABOUT

A dart player scores 83 with three darts hitting a treble, a double and a single (no bulls). Given that the three numbers that he hits add up to 38 and that the difference between the largest and smallest numbers is 9, can you work out how his score is made up?

Treble   Double   Single

136 MIRROR, MIRROR

Which three reversed images belong to Alicia, Bernadette and Claudia, who are shown at the top?

137 SNAPPY

Which one of these six photographs of Mandy was taken as she posed in the bottom left-hand corner?

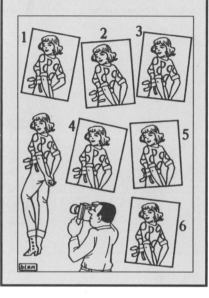

138 RAM-PARTS

The scene shown below is reproduced on the right in twelve pieces, three of which have one detail more and four one detail less than the corresponding part of the original. Which details are extra and which are missing?

139   IN OILS   ★

Which two of these numbered drawings show the same palette and the same picture, which two the same palette but a different picture and which two a different palette but the same picture?

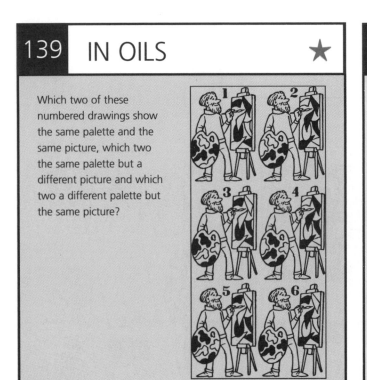

141   WHO'S WHO?   ★

Can you match each man to his brother?

140   DROP-OUT   ★

The man is choosing a T-shirt. In the bottom picture, he's made his choice. Which T-shirt did he buy?

142 PILE UP

These piles of bricks aren't the random results of a child's play but clues to a final, at present blank, pile on the right. Like the rest, that one has six bricks each with a different one of the six letters. The numbers below the heaps tell you two things:

(a) The number of adjacent pairs of bricks in that column which also appear adjacent in the final pile.

(b) The number of adjacent pairs of bricks that make a correct pair but the wrong way up.

So:

 would score one in the 'Correct' row if the final heap had an A directly above a C and a one in the 'Reversed' row if the final heap had a C on top of an A. From all this, can you create the final pile before it topples?

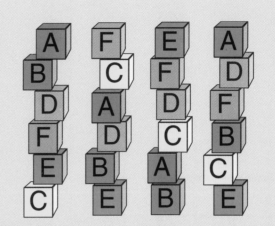

Correct	0	3	0	0		5
Reversed	1	0	0	0		0

143 TSUNAMI

The numbers alongside each row or column tell you how many blocks of black squares are in a line. For example: 2, 3, 5 tells you that from left to right (or top to bottom) there is a group of two black squares, then at least one white space, then a group of three black squares, then at least one white shape, then a group of five black squares. Each block of black squares on the same line must have at least one white square between it and the next block of black squares.

Sometimes it is possible to tell which squares are going to be black without reference to other lines or columns. In the example below, we can deduce that any block of six black squares must incorporate the two central squares:

6 ▢▢▢▢■■▢▢▢▢

Can you complete this tsunami puzzle, to reveal the hidden pattern or picture?

Column clues (left to right):

| 6 | 11 | 14 | 2 1 1 1 3 | 1 2 1 1 3 | 3 2 1 3 | 4 1 1 3 | 1 1 1 3 | 1 1 2 4 | 1 1 2 6 | 1 1 3 | 4 3 | 1 6 | 6 6 | 1 3 1 | 1 1 1 1 | 6 1 1 | 8 1 | 1 2 6 | 3 1 |

Row clues (top to bottom):

| 5 |
| 3 1 1 |
| 2 1 1 1 5 |
| 1 1 5 1 3 |
| 6 1 2 1 |
| 3 1 1 2 1 |
| 4 1 3 1 4 |
| 3 4 1 6 |
| 3 1 1 1 |
| 10 8 |
| 2 2 1 1 |
| 11 6 |
| 13 1 |
| 9 3 1 |
| 2 2 3 1 |

144 LOGI-5 ★★

Each line, across and down, is to have each of the letters A, B, C, D and E, appearing once each. Also, every shape – shown by the thick lines – must also have each of the letters in it. Can you fill in the grid?

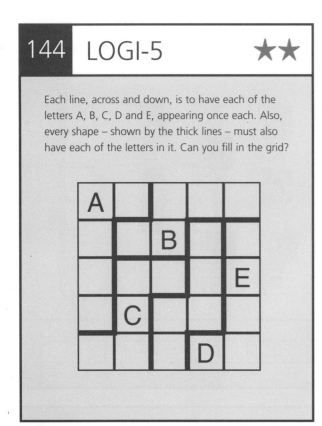

145 ABC ★★

Each line, across and down, is to have each of the letters A, B and C, and two empty squares. The letter outside the grid shows the first or second letter in the direction of the arrow. Can you fill in the grid?

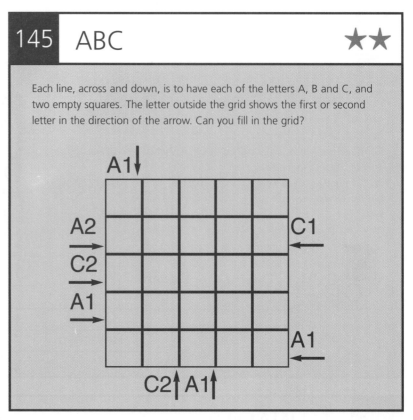

146 DROP-OUT ★

Ten competitors are seen starting the race (left), but only nine of them managed to finish it (right). Which one has dropped out?

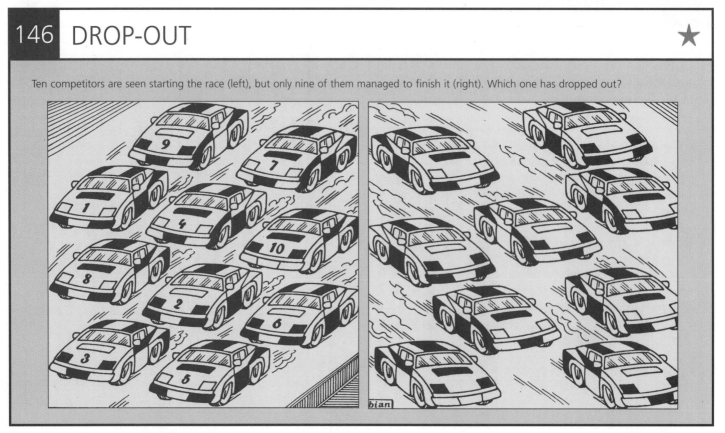

147 TSUNAMI ★★★

The numbers alongside each row or column tell you how many blocks of black squares are in a line. For example: 2, 3, 5 tells you that from left to right (or top to bottom) there is a group of two black squares, then at least one white space, then a group of three black squares, then at least one white shape, then a group of five black squares. Each block of black squares on the same line must have at least one white square between it and the next block of black squares.

Sometimes it is possible to tell which squares are going to be black without reference to other lines or columns. In the example below, we can deduce that any block of six black squares must incorporate the two central squares:

6 

Can you complete this tsunami puzzle, to reveal the hidden pattern or picture?

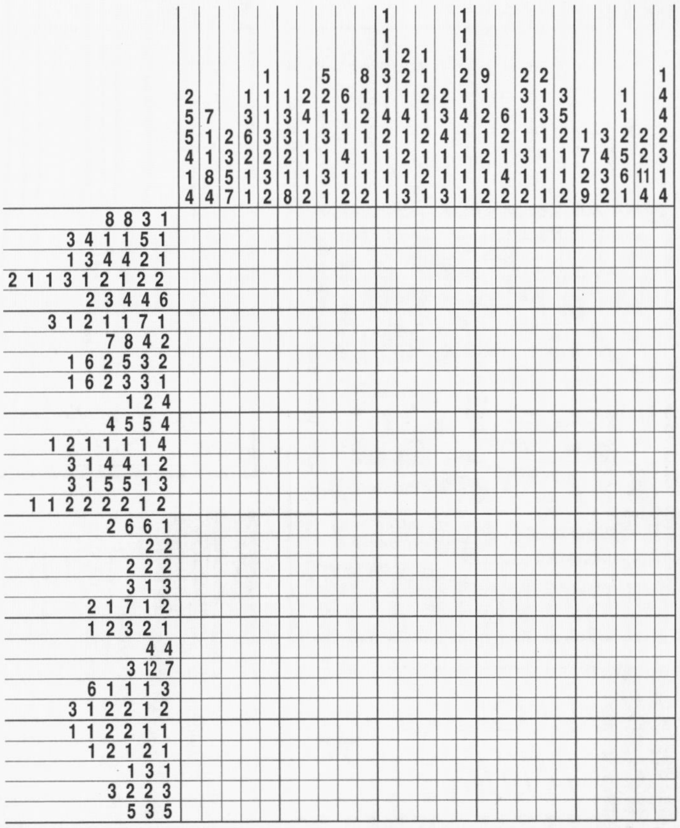
2 5 5 4 1 4
7 1 1 8 4
2 3 5 7
1 3 6 2 1 1
1 1 1 3 2 3 2
1 3 3 2 1 8
2 4 1 1 1 2
5 2 1 3 1 3 1
6 1 1 4 1 2
8 1 2 1 1 1 2
1 1 1 3 1 4 2 1 1 1
2 2 1 4 1 2 1 3
1 1 2 1 2 1 2 1
2 3 4 1 1 3
1 1 1 2 1 4 1 1 1
9 1 2 1 1 2
6 2 1 4 2
2 3 1 1 3 1 2
2 1 3 1 1 1 1
3 5 2 1 1 2
1 7 2 9
3 4 3 2
1 1 2 5 6 1
2 2 11 4
1 4 4 2 3 1 4
8 8 3 1
3 4 1 1 5 1
1 3 4 4 2 1
2 1 1 3 1 2 1 2 2
2 3 4 4 6
3 1 2 1 1 7 1
7 8 4 2
1 6 2 5 3 2
1 6 2 3 3 1
1 2 4
4 5 5 4
1 2 1 1 1 1 4
3 1 4 4 1 2
3 1 5 5 1 3
1 1 2 2 2 2 1 2
2 6 6 1
2 2
2 2 2
3 1 3
2 1 7 1 2
1 2 3 2 1
4 4
3 12 7
6 1 1 1 3
3 1 2 2 1 2
1 1 2 2 1 1
1 2 1 2 1
1 3 1
3 2 2 3
5 3 5

148 SIX-WAY COUNT ★★

How many regular hexagons of all sizes are there in this diagram?

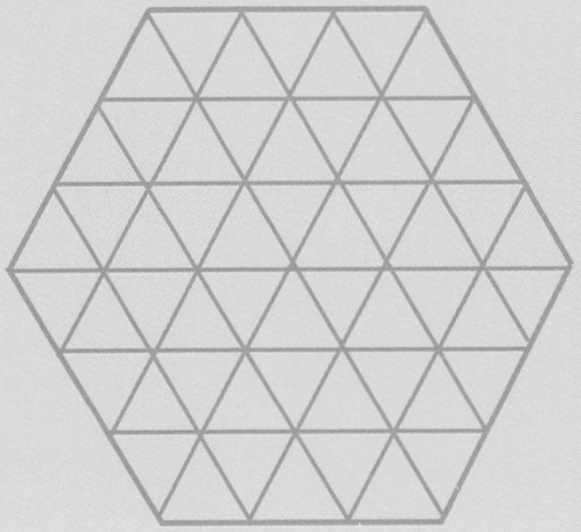

149 WIRED UP ★

Which plug should be inserted in the socket in order for the lamp to work?

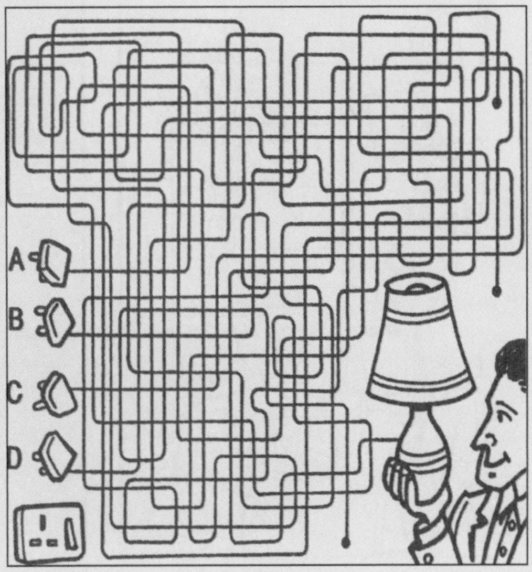
A
B
C
D

150 MAZE WAYS

Which route must each numbered ship take to reach its destination of the same number – without crossing the path of any of the other three?

151 DOT-TO-DOT

Join the dots from 1 to 37 to reveal the hidden picture.

152 SYMBOLIC ★

Which two of the boxes contain the same four symbols?

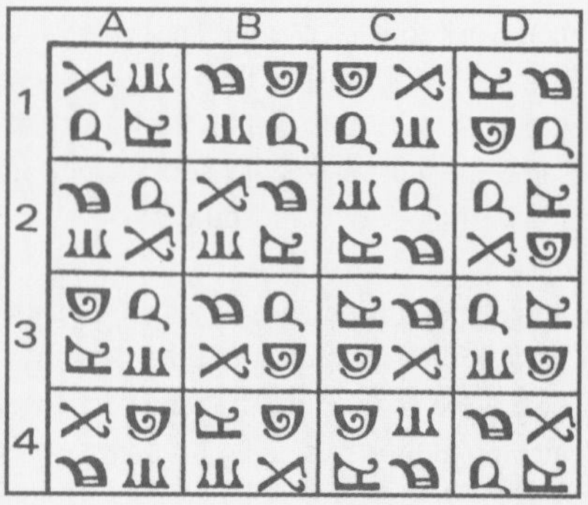

153 BLOCKS AWAY ★

The archaeologist has realised that there will be three blocks missing if he tries to reconstruct the original mural shown. Which ones are they?

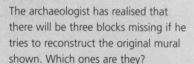

154 TSUNAMI ★★★

The numbers alongside each row or column tell you how many blocks of black squares are in a line. For example: 2, 3, 5 tells you that from left to right (or top to bottom) there is a group of two black squares, then at least one white space, then a group of three black squares, then at least one white shape, then a group of five black squares. Each block of black squares on the same line must have at least one white square between it and the next block of black squares.

Sometimes it is possible to tell which squares are going to be black without reference to other lines or columns. In the example below, we can deduce that any block of six black squares must incorporate the two central squares:

6 □□□□□■■□□□□

Can you complete this tsunami puzzle, to reveal the hidden pattern or picture?

Row clues (top to bottom):

- 22
- 6 17
- 5 8 7
- 5 6 2 3
- 4 5 5 4 1
- 7 4 5 5 1
- 2 3 3 3 1 3
- 1 3 2 4 2
- 1 2 1 3 4 1 2
- 1 2 2 2 1 5 1
- 1 1 3 3 7
- 1 1 7
- 1 1 3 2
- 1 1 2 2 2
- 1 1 1 2 2 2
- 1 1 1 2 2 1
- 1 1 1 2 1 1
- 1 1 1 1 1
- 1 1 1 1
- 1 6 3
- 1 1
- 1 1 1
- 1 8 1
- 1 1 1 1
- 1 6 1
- 1 6 1
- 1 4 2
- 1 1 2
- 1 4 4
- 1 6
- 2 8
- 6 11
- 9 12
- 28

155 SAMPLER ★

A sample has been cut from each of the three rolls of cloth. Which sample belongs to which roll?

bian

156 MAZE WAYS ★

What route has each worker to take in order to get to his or her respective place of work without crossing the path of any of the other three?

157 TSUNAMI ★★

The numbers alongside each row or column tell you how many blocks of black squares are in a line. For example: 2, 3, 5 tells you that from left to right (or top to bottom) there is a group of two black squares, then at least one white space, then a group of three black squares, then at least one white shape, then a group of five black squares. Each block of black squares on the same line must have at least one white square between it and the next block of black squares.

Sometimes it is possible to tell which squares are going to be black without reference to other lines or columns. In the example below, we can deduce that any block of six black squares must incorporate the two central squares:

6

Can you complete this tsunami puzzle, to reveal the hidden pattern or picture?

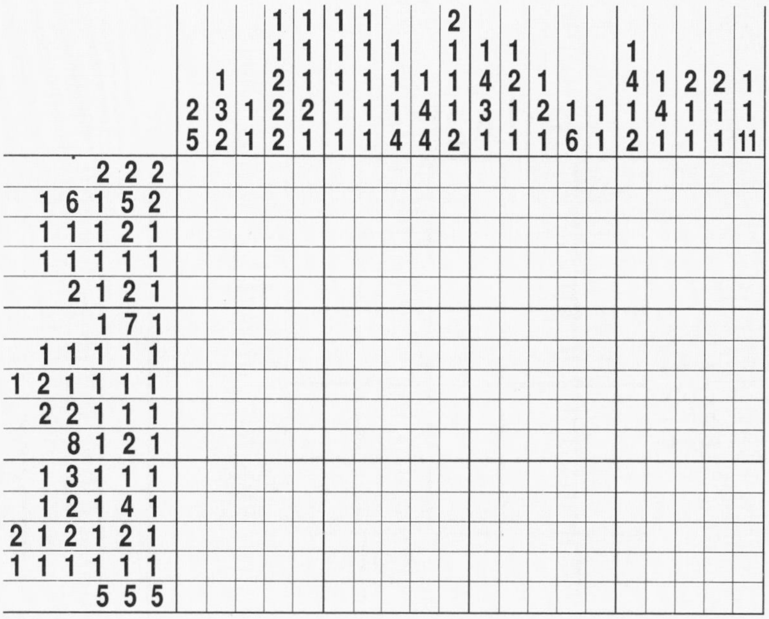

Column clues (read top to bottom per column):

```
                1 1 1 1                 2
          1     1 1 1 1 1     1         2 1   1 1           1
        2 3 1   2 2 1 1 1 1 1 4 2 1     4 3 1 1 2 1 1       1 4 1 2 2 1 1
        5 2 1 2 1 2 1 1 1 4 4 2 1 1 1 6 1 1 2 1 4 1 1 1 1 1 1
```

Row clues:

		Grid
	2 2 2	
1 6	1 5 2	
1 1	1 2 1	
1 1	1 1 1	
	2 1 2 1	
	1 7 1	
1 1	1 1 1	
1 2	1 1 1 1	
2 2	1 1 1	
	8 1 2 1	
1 3	1 1 1	
1 2	1 4 1	
2 1	2 1 2 1	
1 1	1 1 1 1	
	5 5 5	

158 SAFE BET

This is an odd type of safe. If you solve all the clues and enter them in the grid, the correct combination will appear in the shaded squares.

ACROSS
1   Subtract 22,289 from *3 across*
3   4 per cent of 1,111,100
5   Subtract 200 from *6 across*
6   Add 4 to *3 down*
8   Add 526 to *5 across*
10 Square root of 12,321
11 Square first four digits of *25 across*
17 Square first four digits of *1 across*
19 Half of *6 across*
20 Add 13 to *10 across*
21 Last three digits of *1 across*
23 Add 4 to *21 across*
24 Half of *3 across*
25 Add 10,416 to *8 across*

DOWN
1   Square *23 across*
2   Square root of 258,064
3   Square first two digits of *1 across*
4   Twice *1 across*
5   Add 2,368,131 to *4 down*
7   Add 5,783,078 to *5 down*
9   Add 370 to *23 across*, then multiply by 40
12 Subtract 33 from *15 down*
13 Next in series 313, 412, 511, ...
14 Subtract 312 from *3 down*
15 Subtract 260 from *22 down*
16 Multiply *2 down* by 44
18 Add 6 to *3 across*
22 Add 4 to *2 down*
23 Subtract 10 from *10 across*

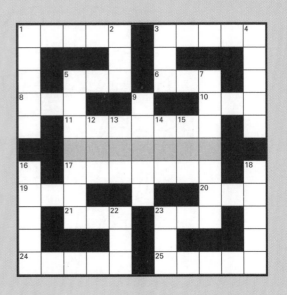

159 ABC

Each line, across and down, is to have each of the letters A, B and C, and two empty squares. The letter outside the grid shows the first or second letter in the direction of the arrow. Can you fill in the grid?

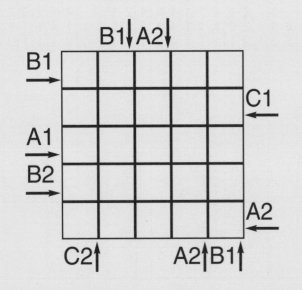

160 TRILINES

Which three straight lines, drawn between opposing reference numbers, divide the rectangle into six parts, each containing three different pairs of animals?

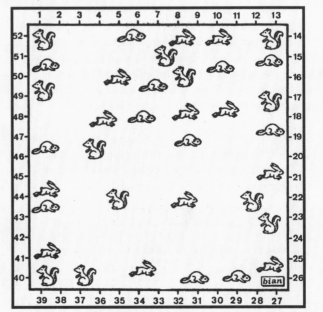

161 | DOMINO SEARCH ★★

A standard set of dominoes has been laid out, using numbers instead of dots for clarity. Using a sharp pencil and a keen brain, can you draw in the lines to show where each domino has been placed? You may find the check grid useful – crossing off each domino as you find it.

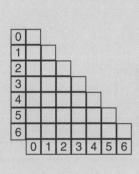

1	0	3	4	5	1	2	4
6	5	0	0	0	2	3	4
3	1	6	1	2	4	4	6
6	1	5	5	0	3	3	2
6	4	0	4	5	6	3	5
5	3	2	1	3	1	0	5
6	0	1	6	2	2	2	4

162 | SHELF LIFE ★

Which one of the six drawers should the handyman choose to match the two already in place?

163 | PILE UP ★★

These piles of bricks aren't the random results of a child's play but clues to a final, at present blank, pile on the right. Like the rest, that one has six bricks each with a different one of the six letters. The numbers below the heaps tell you two things:
(a) The number of adjacent pairs of bricks in that column which also appear adjacent in the final pile.
(b) The number of adjacent pairs of bricks that make a correct pair but the wrong way up.
So:

would score one in the 'Correct' row if the final heap had an A directly above a C and a one in the 'Reversed' row if the final heap had a C on top of an A. From all this, can you create the final pile before it topples?

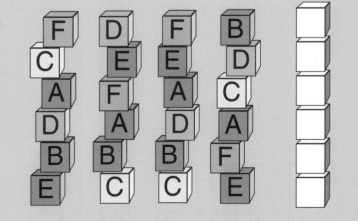

Correct	0	2	1	0	5
Reversed	1	0	1	0	0

164 BLACK OUT ★

Which three insects are shown in silhouette at the top?

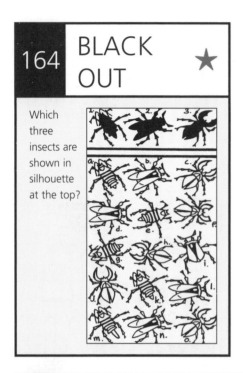

165 POT SHOT ★

Two of these pictures are identical, while each of the others is different in one small detail. Which are the 'twins' and what are the differences?

166 COGITATE ★

Can you see which two weights will rise and which two will fall when the man turns the lever as shown?

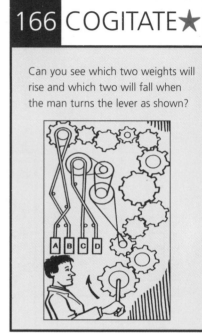

167 BATTLESHIPS ★★

Do you remember the old game of battleships? This puzzle is based on that idea. Your task is to find the vessels in the diagram. Some parts of boats or sea squares have already been filled in, and a number next to a row or column refers to the number of occupied squares in that row or column. The boats may be positioned horizontally or vertically, but no two boats or parts of boats are in adjacent squares – horizontally, vertically or diagonally.

Aircraft carrier: ▢▢▢▢
Battleships: ▢▢ ▢▢
Cruisers: ▢▢ ▢▢ ▢▢
Destroyers: ○ ○ ○ ○

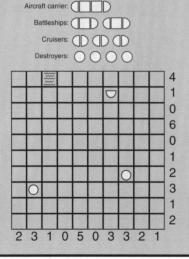

168 TSUNAMI ★★

The numbers alongside each row or column tell you how many blocks of black squares are in a line. For example: 2, 3, 5 tells you that from left to right (or top to bottom) there is a group of two black squares, then at least one white space, then a group of three black squares, then at least one white shape, then a group of five black squares. Each block of black squares on the same line must have at least one white square between it and the next block of black squares.

Sometimes it is possible to tell which squares are going to be black without reference to other lines or columns. In the example below, we can deduce that any block of six black squares must incorporate the two central squares:

6

Can you complete this tsunami puzzle, to reveal the hidden pattern or picture?

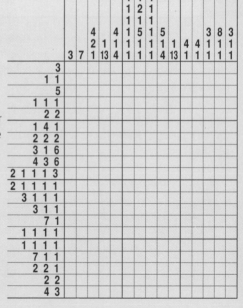

169 SAFE BET

This is an odd type of safe. If you solve all the clues and enter them in the grid, the correct combination will appear in the shaded squares.

ACROSS

1 Multiply 32 by 23
3 Subtract 3,939 from 4,815
5 Multiply 21 by 12
7 Multiply H's alphabetical position by L's
8 Cube 7, add 7
9 Two-nineteenths of 7,467
11 Add a gross, a score and a baker's dozen
13 Minutes between 7.35pm and 2.25am
14 Add 12,345 to 13,033
16 Three-sevenths of 784,917
21 Square 999
22 Add *14 across* to 68,804
25 Divide 4,215 by the square root of 225
27 Treble thirty per cent of 950
28 Subtract 697 from two-thirds of 1,857
30 Add the square root of 729 to 729
31 Number of 'face' cards in 6 packs
32 Divide 9,462 by 19, subtract 99
33 Seventeen per cent of 500, plus 216
34 Square 17, add 605

DOWN

1 Divide 199,850 by 25
2 Add 99,999 to 595,033
4 Pounds in 7 hundredweights and 1 stone
5 A quarter of 5,104 plus a half of 2,474
6 Cube 9, add 4,348
9 Add 3,993,993 to 3,968,932
10 Subtract 1,591,591 from 789,067
12 Multiply 487 by 16, add 100
15 Divide 58,630 by 11
17 Two-thirds of 5,697
18 Add one-seventh of 1,099 to one-eighth of 1,288
19 Divide 16,785 by 9, add 33
20 Quadruple 78,182
23 Multiply *4 down* by 8, subtract 1,805
24 Subtract two-ninths of 8,379 from 3,421
26 Date of start of World War One
29 A score of scores, plus a score

170 TSUNAMI

The numbers alongside each row or column tell you how many blocks of black squares are in a line. For example: 2, 3, 5 tells you that from left to right (or top to bottom) there is a group of two black squares, then at least one white space, then a group of three black squares, then at least one white shape, then a group of five black squares. Each block of black squares on the same line must have at least one white square between it and the next block of black squares.

Sometimes it is possible to tell which squares are going to be black without reference to other lines or columns. In the example below, we can deduce that any block of six black squares must incorporate the two central squares:

Can you complete this tsunami puzzle, to reveal the hidden pattern or picture?

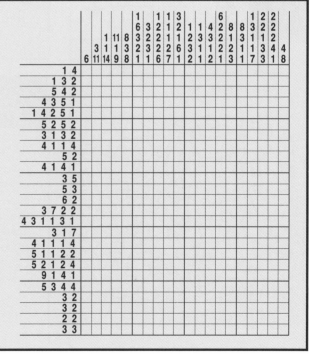

171   ABC   ★★

Each line, across and down, is to have each of the letters A, B and C, and two empty squares. The letter outside the grid shows the first or second letter in the direction of the arrow. Can you fill in the grid?

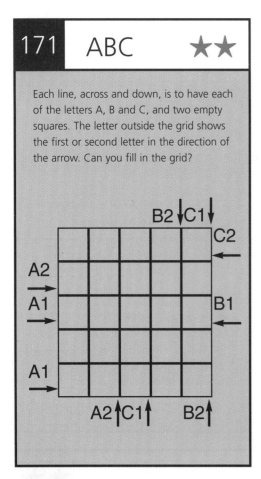

172   THAT LITTLE BIT OF DIFFERENCE   ★

There are eight differences between the two cartoons. Can you spot them?

173   SUM-UP   ★

Calculate the price of each envelope, pot of glue, pencil and roll of tape.

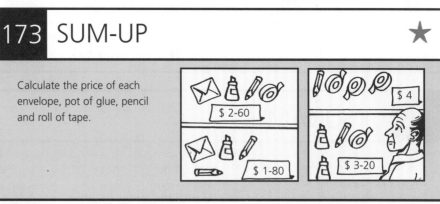

174   SILHOUETTE ★

Shade in every fragment containing a dot – and what have you got?

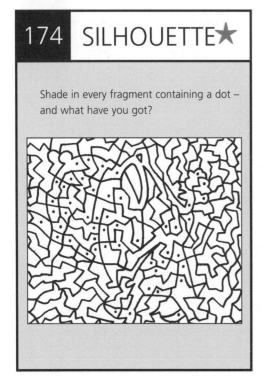

175   BATTLESHIPS   ★★

Do you remember the old game of battleships? These puzzles are based on that idea. Your task is to find the vessels in the diagram. Some parts of boats or sea squares have already been filled in, and a number next to a row or column refers to the number of occupied squares in that row or column. The boats may be positioned horizontally or vertically, but no two boats or parts of boats are in adjacent squares – horizontally, vertically or diagonally.

Aircraft carrier:
Battleships:
Cruisers:
Destroyers:

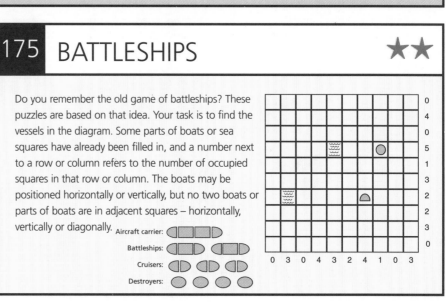

176 TSUNAMI

The numbers alongside each row or column tell you how many blocks of black squares are in a line. For example: 2, 3, 5 tells you that from left to right (or top to bottom) there is a group of two black squares, then at least one white space, then a group of three black squares, then at least one white shape, then a group of five black squares. Each block of black squares on the same line must have at least one white square between it and the next block of black squares.

Sometimes it is possible to tell which squares are going to be black without reference to other lines or columns. In the example below, we can deduce that any block of six black squares must incorporate the two central squares:

6 □□□□■■□□□□

Can you complete this tsunami puzzle, to reveal the hidden pattern or picture?

				2											1							
			1	2	1	1	1	1							1							
		4	5	1	1	2	1	2	1	1	1	1	2		1	2		2	1		
		3	1	2	1	1	2	3	1	1	1	1	1	2	6	1	2	1	2		
		3	1	2	2	4	1	1	2	3	8	6	6	1	6	2	7	2	2		
		2	1	3	2	1	1	3	1	4	2	3	2	2	2	2	2	2	2		
6																						
1 2																						
7 2																						
1 1 1 1 1																						
3 3 1 1																						
1 1 4 4																						
2 3 1 1																						
1 1 1 2																						
1 4 2																						
9 3																						
2 6																						
1 4 5																						
1 4																						
1 3 5 2																						
1 1 1 5																						
1 8 4																						
2 6 5																						
1 1																						
1 2 7																						
5 8																						

177 SHORE THING

Two of these pictures are exactly the same, while each of the other two differs in one small detail from the rest. Can you spot the matching pictures and the differences?

178 NUMBER JIG

Fit the numbers into the grid as quickly as possible. One has been done for you.

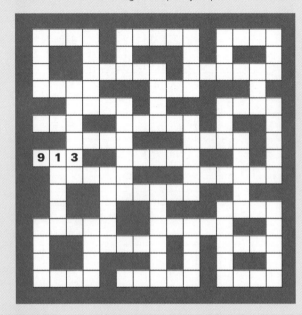

3 figures	4 figures	5 figures	6 figures
157	1670	13556	210954
298	1810	18244	360610
380	2031	25054	540132
541	2085	27305	652224
696	3291	30393	708357
909	4108	31011	880346
(913)	4328	33906	
974	5364	44815	
	6309	49933	
	6312	65248	
	6923	66302	
	7008	68411	
	7623	75120	
	8059	82714	
	8335	83307	
	8790	91369	
	9174	95505	

179 PANDORA'S BOXES ★★★

Pandora Persimmons is the presenter of a quiz show in which successful contestants earn the right to open one of the boxes displayed as in the diagram, the contents of which may prove to be worth having or virtually worthless. Pandora tempts the contestants to forfeit the right to open by offering sums of money, which, in this instance, were refused. From the clues given below, can you indicate in the diagram in what order each of our six qualified to open a box, which box each chose and what it contained?

Clues

1 The order of the contestants did not tally with the number of the box each chose to open.

2 Lynne, who opened box 2, won a cash prize but less than that won by Sharon, whose turn was more than one earlier.

3 Michael, whose turn was next after that of the winner of $100, opened a box more than one place further right than the winner's.

4 The box containing the bar of soap turned out to be next left to the one opened by the fifth contestant; the box chosen by Jim was further left than either.

5 The turn of the contestant who collected the wooden spoon was next before that of the one who was less than ecstatic at winning 50 cents; the box with the spoon in it was next right to the one holding $1,000.

6 Susan opened the box next right to that chosen by Rob, whose turn immediately followed hers.

7 No two men opened adjacent boxes; the winner of the star prize of

$5,000 was the only person whose box was between a man's, on the left, and a woman's, on the right.

Contestants: Jim; Lynne; Michael; Rob; Sharon; Susan
Contents: 50 cents; $100; $1,000; $5,000; bar of soap; wooden spoon

Name: ___ ___ ___ ___ ___ ___
Order: ___ ___ ___ ___ ___ ___
Prize: ___ ___ ___ ___ ___ ___

Starting tip: Work out in which box the $5,000 was hidden.

180 DON'T PAY THE PIPER...

The diagram shows the Pied Piper leading away the children of Hamelin after the town refused to pay him for ridding it of rats. From the clues given below, can you name the first four children in the line, work out their ages, and say what work their father does in the town?

Clues

1 The cowherd's child is directly behind six-year-old Gretchen as they follow the Piper.

2 Hans is younger than Johann.

3 The boy who leads the line is not immediately followed by the butcher's child.

4 The child aged 7 is number 3 in the line.

5 Maria, whose father is an apothecary, is younger than the child in position 2.

Names: Gretchen; Hans; Johann; Maria
Ages: 5; 6; 7; 8
Fathers: apothecary; butcher; cowherd; woodcutter

Pied Piper

Name: ____ ____ ____ ____
Age: ____ ____ ____ ____
Father: ____ ____ ____ ____

Starting tip: Start by placing Gretchen.

181 CHANGE GEAR ★

While putting the final touches to his work, the artist notices that there are five discrepancies between his picture and the model. What are they?

182 WIRED UP ★

Can you work out which of the four plugs is connected to the shaver?

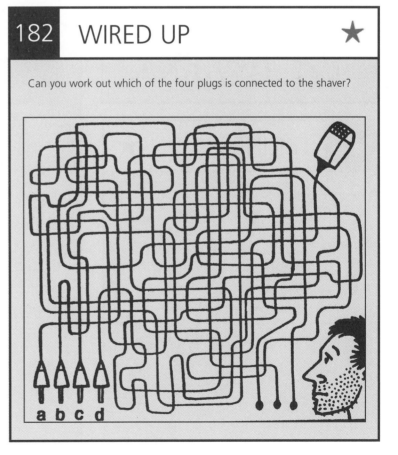

a b c d

183   IN FOCUS   ★

Which of these snaps is actually of the model shown?

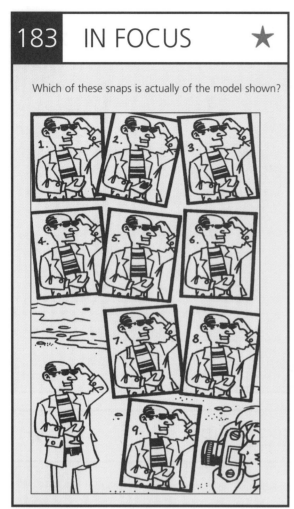

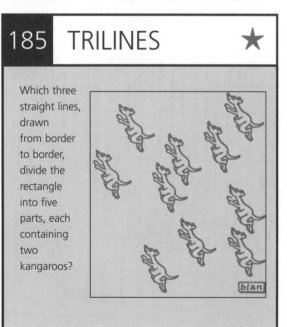

184   CARRY OUT   ★

Each picture is lacking in one detail that is present in the other three. What are they?

185   TRILINES   ★

Which three straight lines, drawn from border to border, divide the rectangle into five parts, each containing two kangaroos?

186   TRIO   ★

Three of the vases on the right are identical.
Can you spot which three?

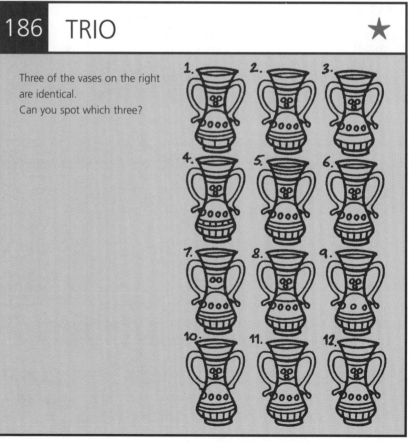

187 COG-ITATE ★

Which one of the two points will be touched when the engineer turns the handle as shown?

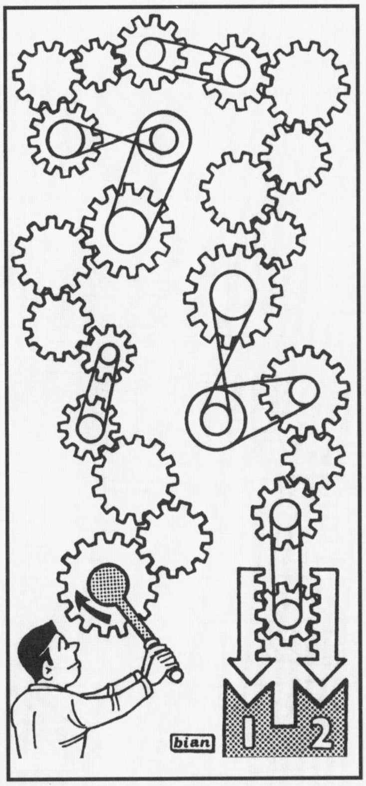
1
2
bian

188 TSUNAMI ★★

The numbers alongside each row or column tell you how many blocks of black squares are in a line. For example: 2, 3, 5 tells you that from left to right (or top to bottom) there is a group of two black squares, then at least one white space, then a group of three black squares, then at least one white shape, then a group of five black squares. Each block of black squares on the same line must have at least one white square between it and the next block of black squares.

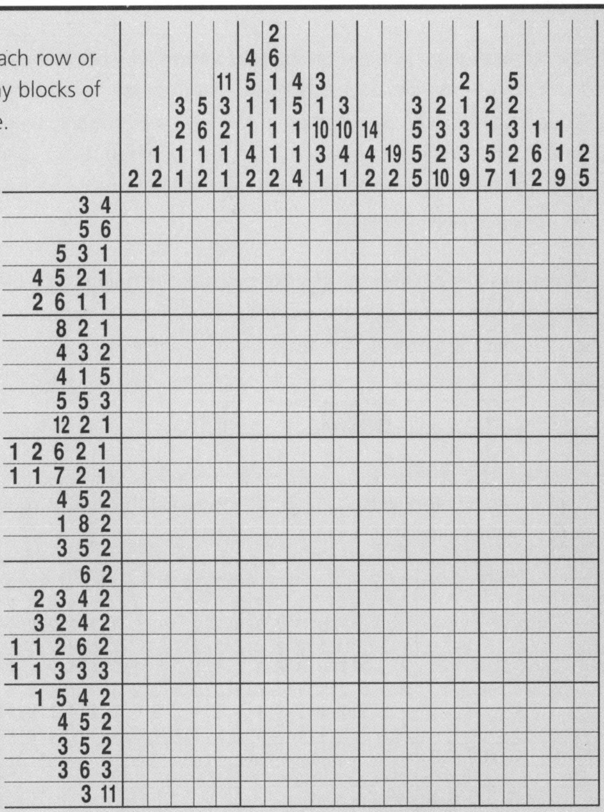
Column clues:
2
1 2
3 2 1 1
5 6 1 2
11 3 2 1 1
4 5 1 1 4 2
2 6 1 1 1 1 2
4 5 1 1 4
3 1 10 3 1
3 10 4 1
14 4 2
19 2
3 5 5 5
2 3 2 10
2 1 3 3 9
2 1 5 7
5 2 3 2 1
1 6 2
1 1 9
2 5
Row clues:
3 4
5 6
5 3 1
4 5 2 1
2 6 1 1
8 2 1
4 3 2
4 1 5
5 5 3
12 2 1
1 2 6 2 1
1 1 7 2 1
4 5 2
1 8 2
3 5 2
6 2
2 3 4 2
3 2 4 2
1 1 2 6 2
1 1 3 3 3
1 5 4 2
4 5 2
3 5 2
3 6 3
3 11

Sometimes it is possible to tell which squares are going to be black without reference to other lines or columns. In the example below, we can deduce that any block of six black squares must incorporate the two central squares:

6 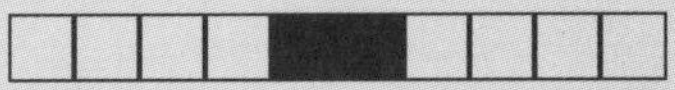

Can you complete this tsunami puzzle, to reveal the hidden pattern or picture?

189 THAT LITTLE BIT OF DIFFERENCE ★

There are eight differences between the two cartoons. Can you spot them?

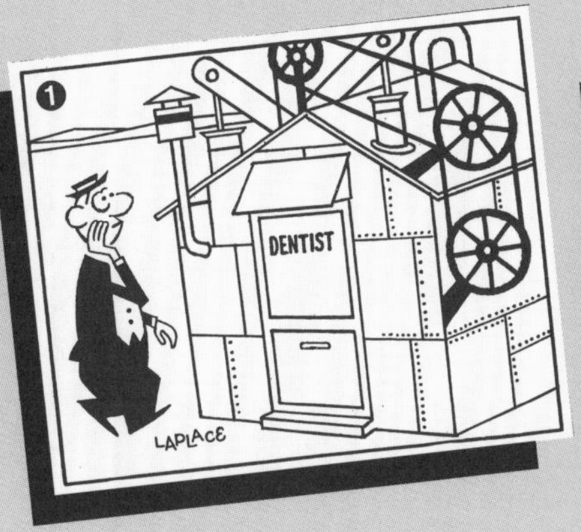
1
DENTIST
LAPLACE

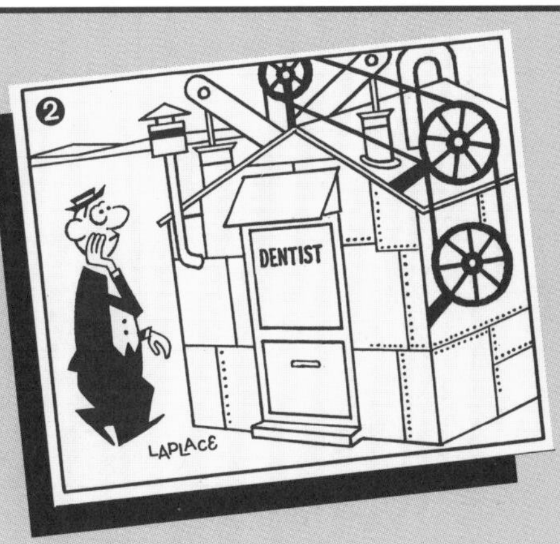
2
DENTIST
LAPLACE

190 TSUNAMI ★★★

The numbers alongside each row or column tell you how many blocks of black squares are in a line. For example: 2, 3, 5 tells you that from left to right (or top to bottom) there is a group of two black squares, then at least one white space, then a group of three black squares, then at least one white shape, then a group of five black squares. Each block of black squares on the same line must have at least one white square between it and the next block of black squares.

Sometimes it is possible to tell which squares are going to be black without reference to other lines or columns. In the example below, we can deduce that any block of six black squares must incorporate the two central squares:

6 ▢▢▢▢■▢▢▢▢

Can you complete this tsunami puzzle, to reveal the hidden pattern or picture?

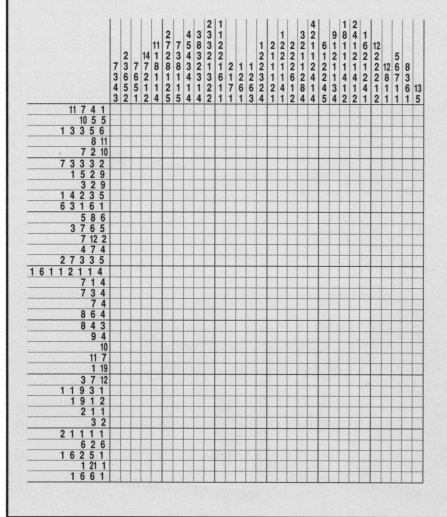

Row clues (top to bottom):
- 11 7 4 1
- 10 5 5
- 1 3 3 5 6
- 8 11
- 7 2 10
- 7 3 3 3 2
- 1 5 2 9
- 3 2 9
- 1 4 2 3 5
- 6 3 1 6 1
- 5 8 6
- 3 7 6 5
- 7 12 2
- 4 7 4
- 2 7 3 3 5
- 1 6 1 1 2 1 1 4
- 7 1 4
- 7 3 4
- 7 4
- 8 6 4
- 8 4 3
- 9 4
- 10
- 11 7
- 1 19
- 3 7 12
- 1 1 9 3 1
- 1 9 1 2
- 2 1 1
- 3 2
- 2 1 1 1 1
- 6 2 6
- 1 6 2 5 1
- 1 21 1
- 1 6 6 1

191 ON THE MARKET   ★

The large picture has been reproduced underneath in twelve pieces. However, three of the pieces contain an extra detail, while four pieces have a detail missing. Can you spot all the extra and missing details?

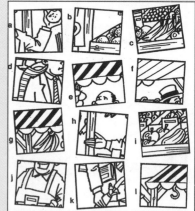

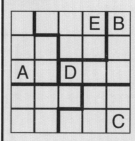

192 LOGI-5 ★★

Each line, across and down, is to have each of the letters A, B, C, D and E, appearing once each. Also, every shape – shown by the thick lines – must also have each of the letters in it. Can you fill in the grid?

Grid:
- Row 1: _, _, _, E, B
- Row 2: _, _, _, _, _
- Row 3: A, _, D, _, _
- Row 4: _, _, _, _, _
- Row 5: _, _, _, _, C

193 SUM-UP ★

Using the totals, calculate the price of each beaker, tube of toothpaste, flannel and bar of soap.

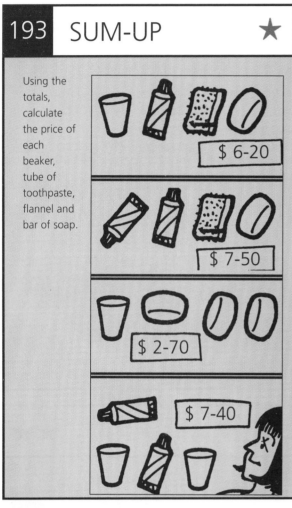

195 LOGICAL ★

Which one of the four numbered pieces should logically replace the question-mark in this design?

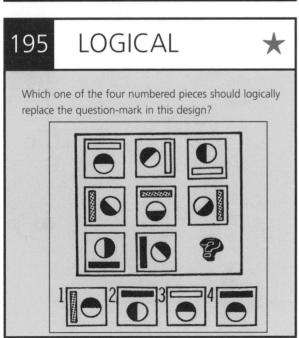

194 SILHOUETTE ★

Shade in every fragment containing a dot – and what have you got?

196 FLIGHT FRIGHT ★

Each picture is lacking in one detail that is present in the other seven. Can you spot these details?

197 ABC ★★

Each line, across and down, is to have each of the letters A, B and C, and two empty squares. The letter outside the grid shows the first or second letter in the direction of the arrow. Can you fill in the grid?

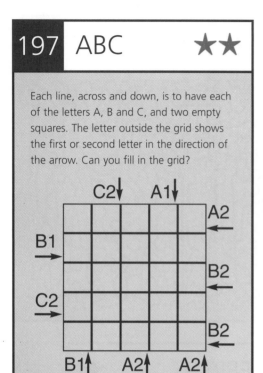

198 DOMINO SEARCH ★★

A standard set of dominoes has been laid out, using numbers instead of dots for clarity. Using a sharp pencil and a keen brain, can you draw in the lines to show where each domino has been placed? You may find the check grid useful – crossing off each domino as you find it.

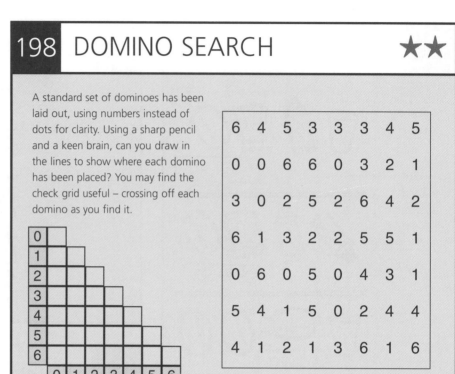

199 BOXED IN ★

Can you see which three objects appear in all four boxes?

200 MAN HUNT ★★

Each hunter A, B, C, D, E has trekked across the frozen waste and is now in his hut – a, b, c, d, e. Naturally, the hut letter corresponds to the hunter's. At no time at all did anyone's tracks cross anyone else's. Nor did anyone cross either lake. Can you show the route each man took?

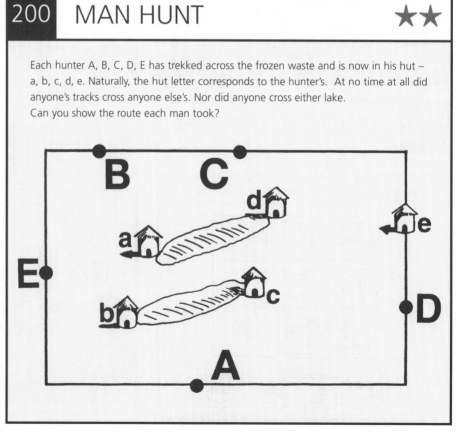

201 LOGI-PATH

Use your deductive reasoning to form a pathway from the box marked START to the box marked FINISH moving in either direction horizontally or vertically (but not diagonally). The number at the beginning of every row or column indicates exactly how many boxes in that row or column your pathway must pass through. The small diagram is given as an example of how it works.

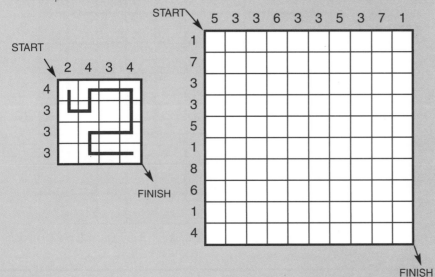

202 NUMBER JIG

Fit the numbers into the grid as quickly as possible. One has been done for you.

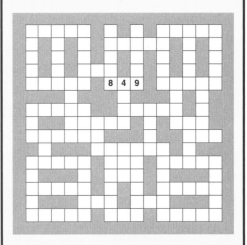

3 figures	5 figures	6 figures
183	10264	142738
186	13956	236007
233	15828	420316
269	21190	523481
311	23104	913345
312	24526	
484	26866	
550	33009	
610	41084	
706	41544	
830	42083	
(849)	43265	
872	51300	
955	51900	
	57134	
	60774	
4 figures	62055	
1002	63044	
3815	63715	
4271	68133	
9928	70222	
	70998	
	71605	
	73930	
	81464	
	81995	
	88921	

203 GUYS IN THE BLACK HATS ★★★

The four posters on the wall of the Sheriff's office in the Wild West town of Redrock show the members of the notorious Black Hat Gang of train-robbers. From the clues given below, can you fill in on the drawing each outlaw's forename, nickname and surname?

Clues
1 Herbert's picture is horizontally adjacent to that of 'Butch' McColl.
2 Poster A shows Jacob, but Silvester Jaggard isn't depicted on poster C.
3 The poster with a picture of the man surnamed Wolf is horizontally adjacent to the one which shows the one nicknamed 'Pony'.
4 Churchman, who appears on poster D, isn't the outlaw nicknamed 'Apache'.

A
First name: _____
Nickname: _____
Surname: _____
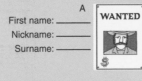

B
_____
_____
_____

C
First name: _____
Nickname: _____
Surname: _____
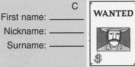

D

Starting tip: Work out the first name of the baddie on poster C.

First names: Herbert; Jacob; Matthew; Silvester
Nicknames: 'Apache'; 'Butch'; 'Pony'; 'Rio'
Surnames: Churchman; Jaggard; McColl; Wolf

204 BATTLESHIPS

Do you remember the old game of battleships? These puzzles are based on that idea. Your task is to find the vessels in the diagram. Some parts of boats or sea squares have already been filled in, and a number next to a row or column refers to the number of occupied squares in that row or column. The boats may be positioned horizontally or vertically, but no two boats or parts of boats are in adjacent squares – horizontally, vertically or diagonally.

Aircraft carrier:

Battleships:

Cruisers:

Destroyers:

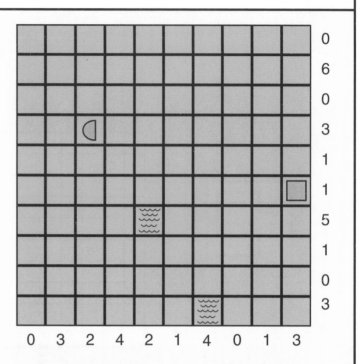

205 MIRROR IMAGE ★

There are four pairs of mirror images above. Can you work out which ones they are, and which figure is the odd one out?

206 BREAD WINNER ★

Two of these pictures are identical, while the other two differ slightly from the rest. Which are the 'twins' and what are the differences?

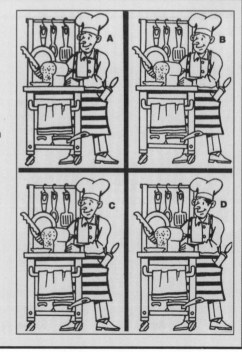

207 HEY PRESTO ★

Can you see which one of the five boxes is the same as that being held by the magician (the two sides are visible in the identical box as well)?

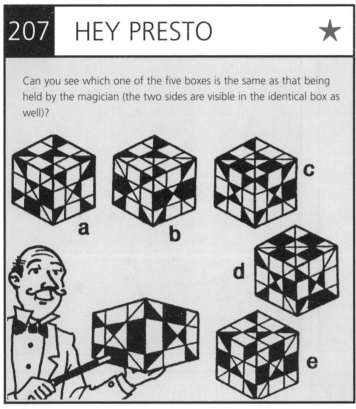

208 FOURSOME ★

This man would like to buy four identical vases. Which design will he choose?

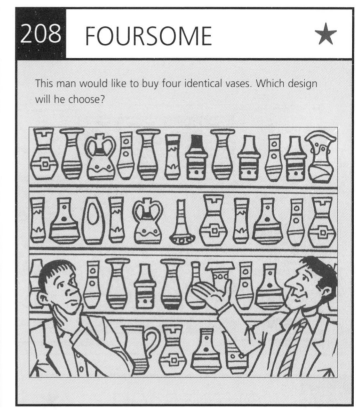

209 VISIGRID ★

Which of the seven impressions was made by the stamp?

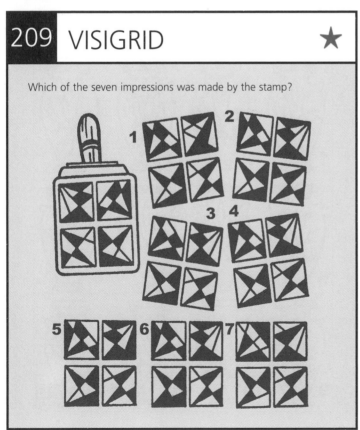

210 SYMBOLIC ★

Can you work out which symbol should logically appear in the empty box and which way up it should be?

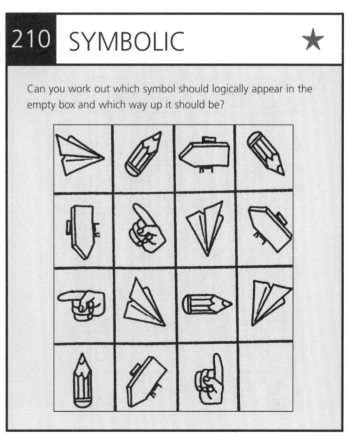

211 CROSSED LINES ★

Which one of these four numbered toy ducks is being pulled by the boy?

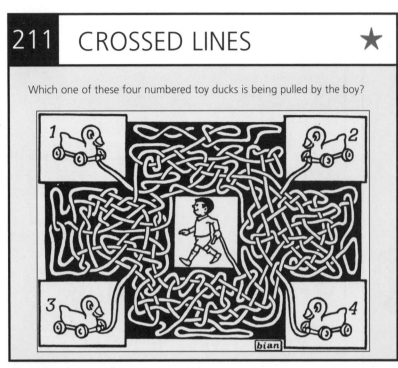

212 DOT-TO-DOT ★

Join the dots from 1 to 42 to reveal the hidden picture.

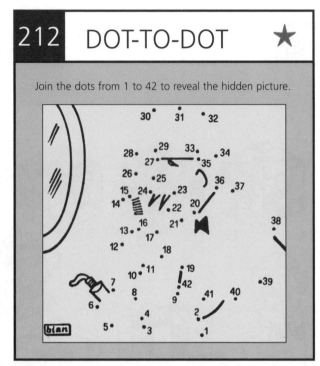

213 LIGHTER FOOL! ★

Four of the six objects shown at the top are hidden in the picture. Which ones are they and in which squares do they appear?

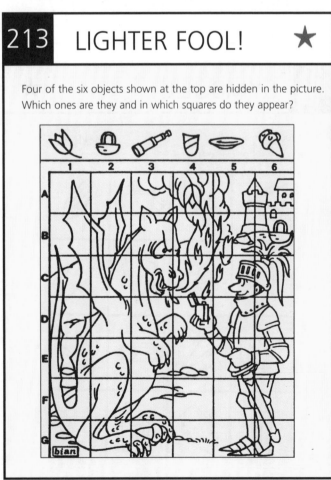

214 URN TURN ★

Which four of the twelve urns are identical?

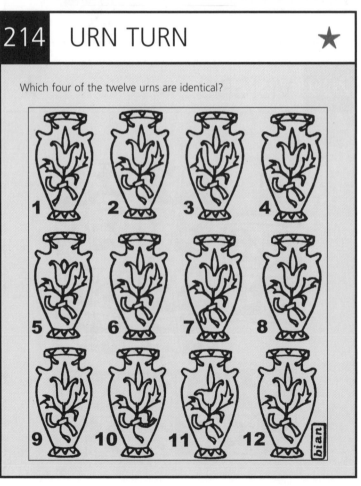

215 TSUNAMI

The numbers alongside each row or column tell you how many blocks of black squares are in a line. For example: 2, 3, 5 tells you that from left to right (or top to bottom) there is a group of two black squares, then at least one white space, then a group of three black squares, then at least one white shape, then a group of five black squares. Each block of black squares on the same line must have at least one white square between it and the next block of black squares.

Sometimes it is possible to tell which squares are going to be black without reference to other lines or columns. In the example below, we can deduce that any block of six black squares must incorporate the two central squares:

6 | | | | | ■ ■ | | | | |

Can you complete this tsunami puzzle, to reveal the hidden pattern or picture?

		1	3		5		6	3	4	4			3	7	4	1	1
		6	2		1	5	1	2	1	1			1	1	1	2	1
		1	1	6	1	1	1	3	1	1	3	3	2	2	4	1	1
		1	1	4	1	1	1	1	2	2	5	1	1	2	2	3	1
	1																
1	5																
	9																
	11																
6	6																
7	3																
1 6	4																
3	2																
2	1																
1 1 1	1																
2 1	2																
3	7																
3 2 2	2																
3	3 3																
3	10																

216 LOCK UP ★

Can you match up the numbered keys with their respective locks?

217 SHELF LIFE ★

Which one of the six numbered drawers will match up with those already in place?

218 PAIR UP ★

Which two flowers are exactly the same?

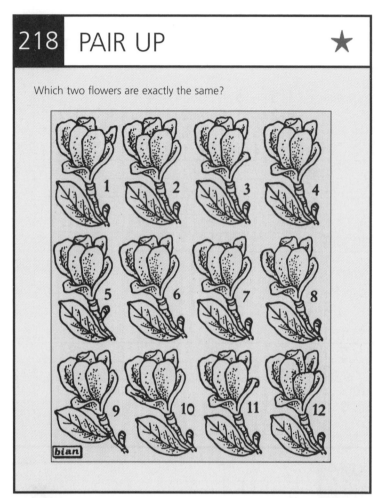

220 CUT UP ★

In what order must the five numbered pieces be arranged to form the complete strip shown at the top?

219 SILHOUETTE ★

Shade in every fragment containing a dot – and what have you got?

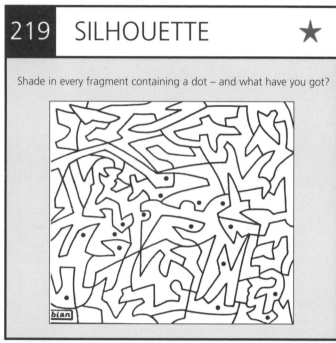

221 BLOCKS AWAY ★

The archaeologist has found that there are three blocks missing when he tries to reconstruct the original mural shown in the top right-hand corner. Which ones are they?

222 SHOPPING AROUND

The bottom picture was taken only a few minutes after the top one. In that time, ten people have been into various shops and bought something – some are even wearing their purchases. Which are the ten shoppers and what have they bought?

223 WHO'S WHO? ★

Using the information given, match each man to his wife.

224 WOODEN HEART ★

Each picture is lacking in one detail that is present in the other seven. What are those details?

225 TSUNAMI

The numbers alongside each row or column tell you how many blocks of black squares are in a line. For example: 2, 3, 5 tells you that from left to right (or top to bottom) there is a group of two black squares, then at least one white space, then a group of three black squares, then at least one white shape, then a group of five black squares. Each block of black squares on the same line must have at least one white square between it and the next block of black squares.

Sometimes it is possible to tell which squares are going to be black without reference to other lines or columns. In the example below, we can deduce that any block of six black squares must incorporate the two central squares:

Can you complete this tsunami puzzle, to reveal the hidden pattern or picture?

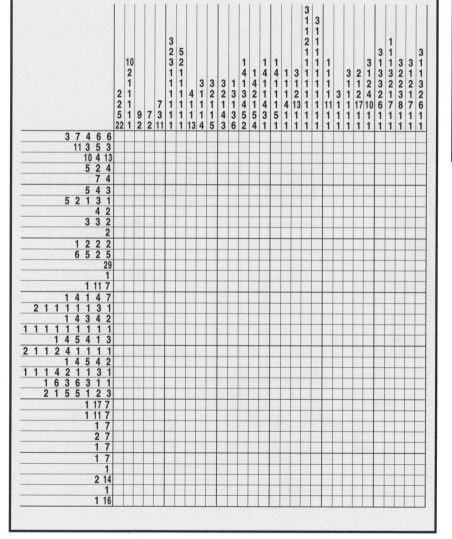

226 ABC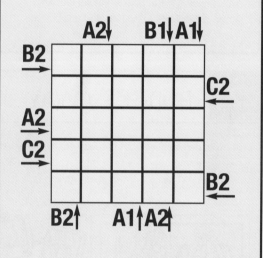

Each line, across and down, is to have each of the letters A. B and C, and two empty squares. The letter outside the grid shows the first or second letter in the direction of the arrow. Can you fill in the grid?

227 TENTACKLE ★★

Eight children are camping out, two to each tent, and some have given us a couple of clues as to how to find them. The trouble is their directions are as bad as their cooking and in each case only one direction is true whilst the other is an exact opposite, so that East should read West etc. Directions are not necessarily exact so North could be North, Northeast or Northwest. To help you one child is already tucked into a sleeping bag.

Ros says: I'm South of Sue and East of Xena.
Una says: I'm North of Zoe and West of Ros.
Viv says: I'm North of Wendy and West of Una.
Xena: I'm South of Trish and East of Sue.

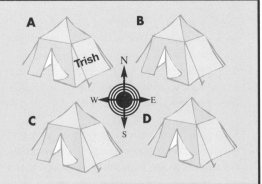

228 BLOCKS AWAY ★

This puzzled archaeologist has realised that there will be three blocks missing if he tries to reconstruct the original mural shown at the top left. Which ones are they?

229 BATTLESHIPS ★★

Do you remember the old game of battleships? This puzzle is based on that idea. Your task is to find the vessels in the diagram. Some parts of boats or sea squares have already been filled in, and a number next to a row or column refers to the number of occupied squares in that row or column. The boats may be positioned horizontally or vertically, but no two boats or parts of boats are in adjacent squares – horizontally, vertically or diagonally.

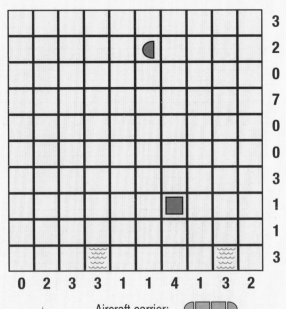

Aircraft carrier:
Battleships:
Cruisers:
Destroyers:

230 HIDE AND SEEK

Four of the six objects lined up at the top are hidden in the picture. Can you see which ones and whereabouts they are?

231 IN THE ABSTRACT ★

George has bought one of the four abstract paintings at the top, but he can't remember which one it is or which way up it should go. Can you help him?

232 TSUNAMI ★★★

The numbers alongside each row or column tell you how many blocks of black squares are in a line. For example: 2, 3, 5 tells you that from left to right (or top to bottom) there is a group of two black squares, then at least one white space, then a group of three black squares, then at least one white shape, then a group of five black squares. Each block of black squares on the same line must have at least one white square between it and the next block of black squares.

Sometimes it is possible to tell which squares are going to be black without reference to other lines or columns. In the example below, we can deduce that any block of six black squares must incorporate the two central squares:

Can you complete this tsunami puzzle, to reveal the hidden pattern or picture?

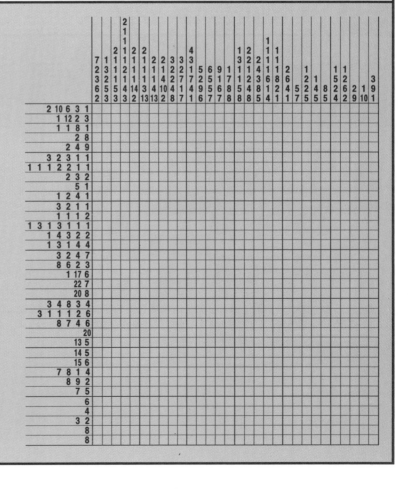

233 DOMINO SEARCH ★★

A standard set of dominoes has been laid out, using numbers instead of dots for clarity. Using a sharp pencil and a keen brain, can you draw in the lines to show where each domino has been placed? You may find the check grid useful – crossing off each domino as you find it.

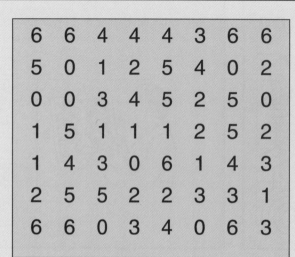

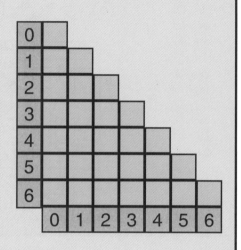

234 NUMBER JIG ★★

Fit the numbers into the grids as quickly as possible. One has been done for you.

3 figures	7704	569857
179	8817	646303
331		802208
(407)	**5 figures**	851707
523	18260	912661
658	24887	978522
669	42325	
918	43148	**7 figures**
	85239	1233067
		1694459
4 figures		2116689
1646	**6 figures**	3428729
2375	119715	7455454
3498	122552	8973135
4582	193277	9301231
4981	225463	
5259	280648	
6144	337594	
7076	445717	

235 RACE WINNERS ★

The large picture shows the start of a race and the small picture shows the eventual finishers. Can you identify them?

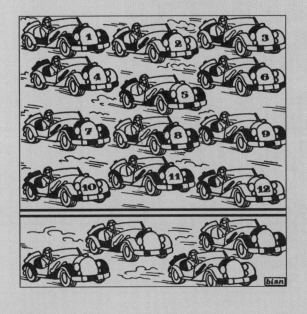

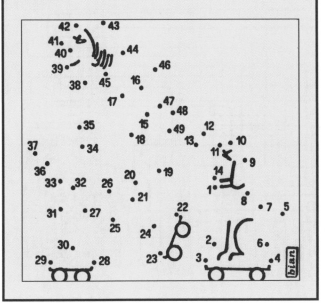

237 DOT TO DOT ★

Join the dots from 1 to 49 to reveal the hidden picture.

236 TSUNAMI ★★

The numbers alongside each row or column tell you how many blocks of black squares are in a line. For example: 2, 3, 5 tells you that from left to right (or top to bottom) there is a group of two black squares, then at least one white space, then a group of three black squares, then at least one white shape, then a group of five black squares. Each block of black squares on the same line must have at least one white square between it and the next block of black squares.

Sometimes it is possible to tell which squares are going to be black without reference to other lines or columns. In the example below, we can deduce that any block of six black squares must incorporate the two central squares:

Can you complete this tsunami puzzle, to reveal the hidden pattern or picture?

Column clues (read top to bottom):

```
                        1
                        2           2
                        2       1   2
                        1       2   2
          1 1 1 2 3 1   1   1               3 4
          1 1 1 5 2 2   1   1               3 2
          1 1 4 2 2 1   1   1       8       2 2     3 2
        1 1 1 1 5 3 3   1   1 1 1 1 2 2 3 1 1 1 1 1
        7 8 7 8 6 6 5   5   4 4 4 4 4 2 5 5 6 5 5 5 5 5
```

Row clues (read left to right):

Clue
1 1 4
1 6
8
4 1 2
9 1 1 1
9 1
1 8
1 1 1 1
2 1 1 1 1 1 1
4 1 1 1 1
6 5 1
4 2 1 1 3
4 3 3 4 2
5 3 4 3
6 6 4
6 7
17
5 8
13
4 6

238 FOURSOME ★

Which four of the twelve vases are identical?

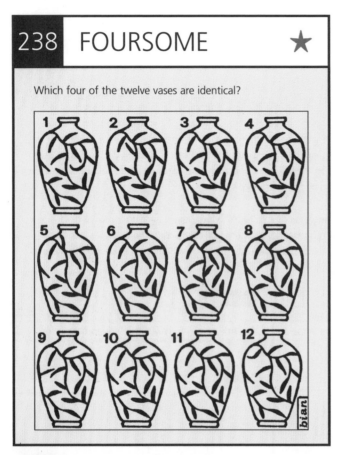

239 BLACK OUT ★

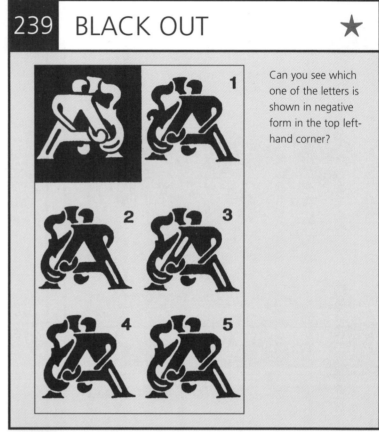

Can you see which one of the letters is shown in negative form in the top left-hand corner?

240 SILHOUETTE ★

Shade in every fragment containing a dot – and what have you got?

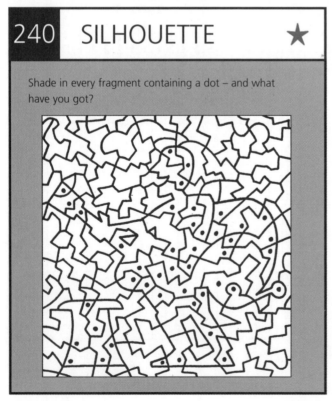

241 WIRED UP ★

Which of the four plugs is connected to the toothbrush?

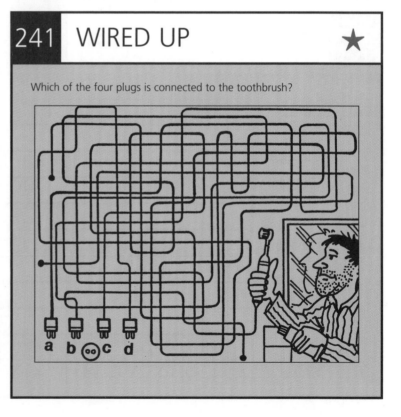

242 DROP OUT

In the picture on the left, the man is selecting a suitcase. In the right-hand picture, he has made his choice. Which did he choose?

243 BATTLESHIPS ★★

Do you remember the old game of battleships? This puzzle is based on that idea. Your task is to find the vessels in the diagram. Some parts of boats or sea squares have already been filled in, and a number next to a row or column refers to the number of occupied squares in that row or column. The boats may be positioned horizontally or vertically, but no two boats or parts of boats are in adjacent squares – horizontally, vertically or diagonally.

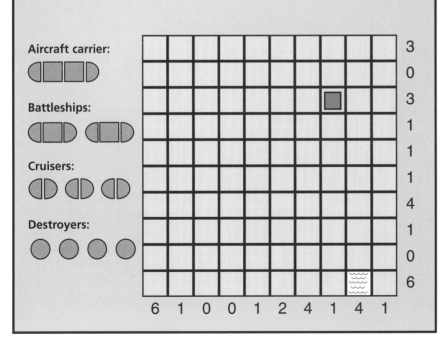

Aircraft carrier:

Battleships:

Cruisers:

Destroyers:

3
0
3
1
1
1
4
1
0
6

6 1 0 0 1 2 4 1 4 1

244 COG-ITATE ★

If the engineer turns the handle in a clockwise direction, which one of the two numbered contacts will be touched?

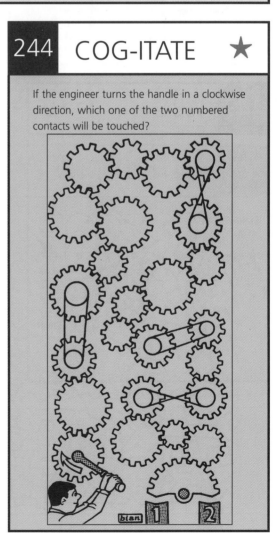

245 LOGI-5 ★★

Each line, across and down, is to have each of the letters A, B, C, D and E, appearing once each. Also, every shape – shown by the thick lines – must also have each of the letters in it. Can you fill in the grid?

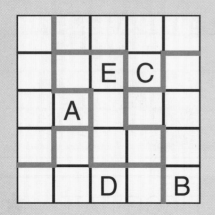

247 ABC ★

Find your way across the clock-faces. watch out for the clock-hands blocking the way.

246 TSUNAMI ★★★

The numbers alongside each row or column tell you how many blocks of black squares are in a line. For example: 2, 3, 5 tells you that from left to right (or top to bottom) there is a group of two black squares, then at least one white space, then a group of three black squares, then at least one white shape, then a group of five black squares. Each block of black squares on the same line must have at least one white square between it and the next block of black squares.

Sometimes it is possible to tell which squares are going to be black without reference to other lines or columns. In the example below, we can deduce that any block of six black squares must incorporate the two central squares:

6 □□□□■■□□□□

Can you complete this tsunami puzzle, to reveal the hidden pattern or picture?

Row clues:

1 5	
8	
8	
13	
1 4	
1 1 4	
1 2 2	
1 1 2	
1 1	
3 3	
3 1	
3 2	
3 1 1	
8 3 1 2	
1 2 1 1 2 5	
2 3 3 1 7	
1 3 2 1 14	
1 1 3 16	
5 3 18	
5 7 16	
1 3 4 15	
4 1	
2 1	
1 2 1	
3 1 10	
2 2 2 2 1 1 1	
3 1 3 3	
1 1 1 1 1 3	
1 1 3 1 3 1	
4 3 6 1 3 1 1 1 2	
3 5 2 3 1 3 1	
3 1 6 1 1 2	
4 1 6 7 7 1	
1 6 1 1 1 1 1 1 3	
1 6 6 7 6 4	

248 FIGURE IT OUT

Each digit from 1–9 appears four times in the square, no similar digits being diagonally adjacent. Where the same digit appears more than once in any row or column, this is stated. Can you complete the square?

Row
1 Two 4s and two 9s; total 34
2 One even, two odd, two even, one odd digit from left to right; lowest is 2; total 37
3 Two 1s separated by an 8; two 5s but no 4s
4 Two adjacent 6s with an odd digit and two 8s
5 Two 3s separated by a 6; highest is a 7; total 22
6 Two adjacent 7s; total 24

Column
1 Two 8s separated by an odd digit; total 29
2 Two adjacent 9s; the other digits also total 18
3 Two adjacent 2s; total 27
4 Two 9s separated by two digits; total 31
5 Two 6s separated by two digits, all bracketed by two odd digits
6 Total 22

249 DOMINO SEARCH ★★

A standard set of dominoes has been laid out, using numbers instead of dots for clarity. Using a sharp pencil and a keen brain, can you draw in the lines to show where each domino has been placed? You may find the check grid useful – crossing off each domino as you find it.

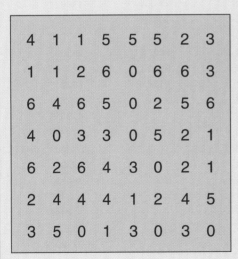

250 MINIMAZE

Each obstacle along the maze's path carries a penalty (as shown in the key in the middle). Find your way from A to B incurring no more penalties than we did – 36 in all.

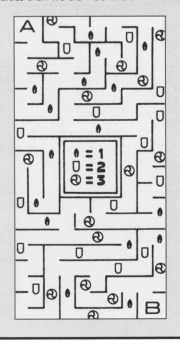

251 IN THE STALLS

The four central seats in each of the first three rows of the stalls at the theatre were all occupied at a recent performance. From the clues given below, can you place each of the listed people in their correct seats?

Clues

1 Peter was sitting directly behind Angela, and somewhere diagonally in front of Henry.

2 Nina had the ticket for seat 12 in row B.

3 The four seats featured in each row are occupied by two males and two females.

4 Maxine is two places to the right of Robert in the same row of the stalls.

5 Judy, who is immediately behind Charles, has her husband Vincent as her right-hand neighbour.

6 One of the men in the audience is sitting in seat 13 of row A.

7 Tony, Janet and Lydia all have seats in different rows of the stalls, the latter having a male neighbour to her left.

Names: Angela; Charles; Henry; Janet; Judy; Lydia; Maxine; Nina; Peter; Robert; Tony; Vincent.

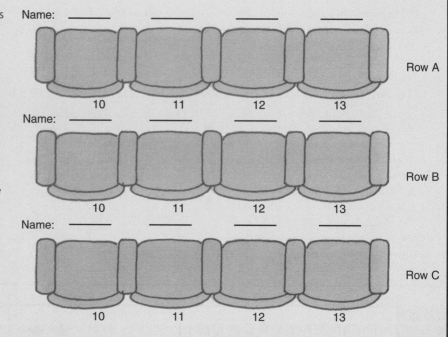

Name: _____

10   11   12   13   Row A

Name: _____

10   11   12   13   Row B

Name: _____

10   11   12   13   Row C

Starting tip: Begin by naming the man in seat 13 of row A.

252 NUMBER JIG

Fit the numbers into the grid as quickly as possible. One has been done for you.

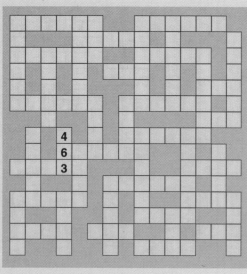

3 figures	4 figures	5 figures	6 figures
237	1243	11188	138924
431	1390	30128	183134
463	2366	48298	237810
598	2395	50021	265805
612	3408	73606	327460
706	4014	81834	382412
813	5018	82610	427894
934	5106		439013
	6362		509307
	7290		552609
	7910		635081
	9306		790296
			808334
			812847
			933321
			972801

253 TSUNAMI ★★★

The numbers alongside each row or column tell you how many blocks of black squares are in a line. For example: 2, 3, 5 tells you that from left to right (or top to bottom) there is a group of two black squares, then at least one white space, then a group of three black squares, then at least one white shape, then a group of five black squares. Each block of black squares on the same line must have at least one white square between it and the next block of black squares.

Sometimes it is possible to tell which squares are going to be black without reference to other lines or columns. In the example below, we can deduce that any block of six black squares must incorporate the two central squares:

Can you complete this tsunami puzzle, to reveal the hidden pattern or picture?

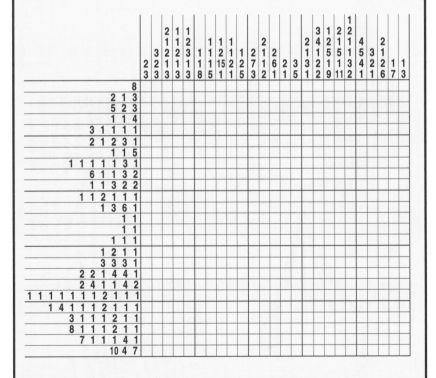

254 WHO'S WHO? ★

From the information given below can you match each man to his wife?

255 TWINNED UP ★

This woman would like to buy a pair of matching vases. Can you help her choose two identical vases?

256   WILHELMANIA

Each picture is lacking in one detail that is present in the other seven. What are those details?

257   KNOT OR NOT ★

Which tangles will knot, and which will not, when their ends are pulled?

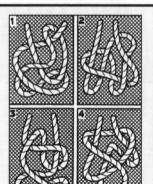

258   SOMNAMBULIC

Our distracted artist has made five mistakes while drawing this picture. Can you spot them?

259   SUMMIT   ★

Go from the top of this pyramid (1) to its base, adding one block's value at each level to get the total of 55. You can only move from a block to one of its two lower neighbours.

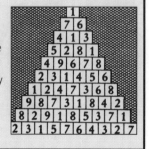

260 | TSUNAMI   ★★★

The numbers alongside each row or column tell you how many blocks of black squares are in a line. For example: 2, 3, 5 tells you that from left to right (or top to bottom) there is a group of two black squares, then at least one white space, then a group of three black squares, then a group of five black squares. Each block of black squares on the same line must have at least one white square between it and the next block of black squares.

Sometimes it is possible to tell which squares are going to be black without reference to other lines or columns. In the example below, we can deduce that any block of six black squares must incorporate the two central squares:

6 ▢▢▢▢■▢▢▢▢

Can you complete this tsunami puzzle, to reveal the hidden pattern or picture?

Row clues (top to bottom):
```
6
5 1 1 2
7 1 4 2 1
7 1 1 4
2 1 1 1 1 2
3 2 1
2 1 1
2 4 1
2 2 2
2 5
2 2 1
2 18
6 3 1
9 1 1
8 17
8 2 1 1
8 1 1 1 1
1 6 4 1 2
1 1 1 2 1 2
1 1 1 2 1 2
1 1 1 5
1 1 1 3
1 1 2 1 1 2
2 1 1 1 1 1
12 5 1 1
1 1 1 4 1
12 1 1 1
1 1 1 1 2 6
2 6 7 3
2 6 9
2 6 11
2 6 13
2 6 15
2 6 17
2 6 19
```

---

261 | FITBITS   ★

The shoppers are enjoying the last minute rush at the sales. Can you work out which two of the five details on the left belong to two of the bargain-hunters?

---

262 | CARTWHEELS   ★

Which two numbered fragments complete wheel A, and which two complete wheel B?

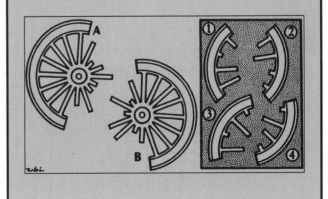

263 MEN AT WORK ★

Four of the six objects shown at the top can be found in the larger picture. Can you see which ones and where they are?

264 TRILINES ★

Which three lines drawn from edge to edge divide the rectangle into five parts, each containing two ducklings?

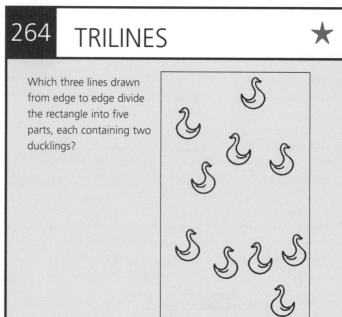

265 IDENTICAL TWINS ★

Have a look at these eight unfortunate victims of the plague. Two of these poor creatures are as sick as each other. Can you find the two identical pictures?

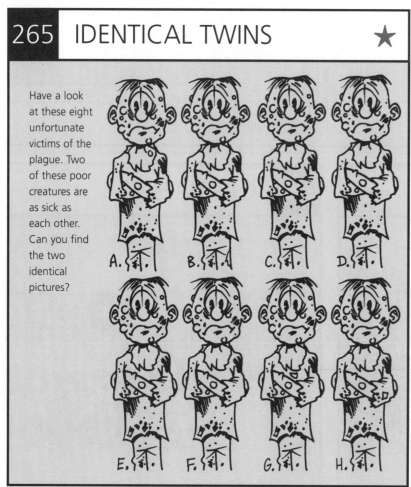

266 ABC ★★

Each line, across and down, is to have each of the letters A, B and C, and two empty squares. The letter outside the grid shows the first or second letter in the direction of the arrow. Can you fill in the grid?

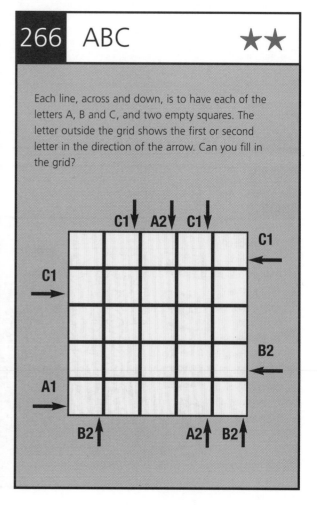

267 A-MAZING ★

Daisy and Joe are starring in the school play as the horse. But Daisy is late and Joe has lost all seven bits of the costume! Help them out by finding the quickest route to the theatre, picking up all the bits of costume on the way.

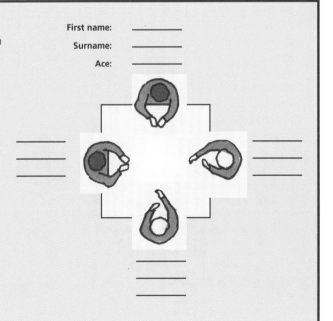

268 ACES HIGH ★★★

The four bridge players sitting round the table each had the Ace of a different suit in his or her hand on the deal in question. From the clues given below, can you fully identify the player in each of the four seats, and work out which Ace each holds? NB North and South play as partners against East and West.

Clues
1 Richard's Ace was the same colour as the one held by Ruff, who was in the North seat.
2 Martina's partner was holding the Ace of Hearts.
3 The woman sitting West, whose surname is not Tenace, had the Ace of Spades.
4 Paul Hand was partnering Esther.
5 The Ace of Clubs was not held by the player sitting South.

First names: Esther; Martina; Paul; Richard
Surnames: Hand; Ruff; Tenace; Trick
Aces: Clubs; Diamonds; Hearts; Spades

Starting tip: Begin by working out which Ace Richard held.

First name: _____
Surname: _____
Ace: _____

269 VIVE LA FRANCE   ★★★

Each of the seventeen squares in the figure in the diagram contains one of the letters which form the name NAPOLEON BONAPARTE, in recognition of the French National Day celebrated on July 14th. From the clues given below, can you insert all seventeen letters in their correct squares?

Clues

1   None of the letters which occur more than once in the name is immediately adjacent in any direction, including diagonally, to one of its duplicates.

2   The letter in the centre of the middle row is T; it has a consonant directly above it.

3   The diagonal sequence O P A appears somewhere in the layout reading downwards from right to left.

4   Neither of the two end squares of the middle row contains a vowel.

5   The letters at the left-hand end of both the top and bottom rows are identical.

6   The three As are all in different rows, and two of them have an N diagonally immediately above and to the left of them.

7   Both Es are in the same row.

8   The pairing N P occurs in one of the rows, reading left to right.

9   None of the columns reading downwards forms an English three-letter word.

10   The L, which has a consonant as its right-hand neighbour, is in the row above the B.

Letters to be inserted: A; A; A; B; E; E; L; N; N; N; O; O; O; P; P; R; T

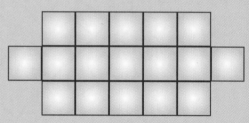

Starting tip:
Begin by placing the sequence referred to in clue 3.

270 TSUNAMI   ★★★

The numbers alongside each row or column tell you how many blocks of black squares are in a line. For example: 2, 3, 5 tells you that from left to right (or top to bottom) there is a group of two black squares, then at least one white space, then a group of three black squares, then at least one white shape, then a group of five black squares. Each block of black squares on the same line must have at least one white square between it and the next block of black squares.

Sometimes it is possible to tell which squares are going to be black without reference to other lines or columns. In the example below, we can deduce that any block of six black squares must incorporate the two central squares:

6 [ ][ ][ ][ ][■][ ][ ][ ] squares:

Can you complete this tsunami puzzle, to reveal the hidden pattern or picture?

Row clues (top to bottom):

Row clues
2 4 3 3
2 2 1 1 1 5
1 1 5 1 1 5
5 3 2 2 2 5
1 2 2 1 1 1 3
1 1 1 1 1 4
1 4 3 1 1 1 1 5
1 1 2 1 1 1 1 2 1 1 1
1 1 2 1 1 1 1 1 1 2 2
2 2 1 1 2 3 2 2
1 2 2 1 1 1 4 3
1 3 2 1 1 2 2 1
2 1 1 2 1
3 1 5 2 1 1
3 2 1 1
3 1 1 1
3 1 1 1
4 6 1
4 6 1
6 5 8
12 1 2 6 1
1 2 8
3 2 3 5 6
1 2 4 1 1 1 6
6 6
1 2 3 1 1 1 6
2 3 4 6 6
4 1 1 1
2 2 2 4 1 1 1
2 3 3 2 2 7

271 PILE UP ★★

These piles of bricks aren't the random results of a child's play but clues to a final, at present blank, pile on the right. Like the rest, that one has six bricks each with a different one of the six letters. The numbers below the heaps tell you two things:

(a) The number of adjacent pairs of bricks in that column which also appear adjacent in the final pile.

(b) The number of adjacent pairs of bricks that make a correct pair but the wrong way up.

So: would score one in the 'Correct' row if the final heap had an A directly above a C and a one in the 'Reversed' row if the final heap had a C on top of an A. From all this, can you create the final pile before it topples?

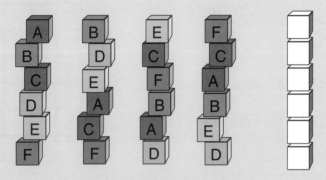

Correct	0	1	1	0		5
Reversed	0	1	2	0		0

272 FILLING IN ★★

Each of the nine empty boxes contains a different digit from 1 to 9. Each calculation is to be treated sequentially rather than according to the 'multiplication first' system. Can you fill in the empty boxes?

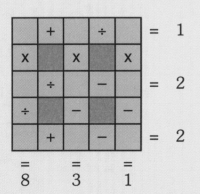

273 PYRAMID ★

Which one of the numbered pieces of paper will, when folded, combine with the four-sided base at the top left to form a pyramid?

274 DOMINO SEARCH ★★

A standard set of dominoes has been laid out, using numbers instead of dots for clarity. Using a sharp pencil and a keen brain, can you draw in the lines to show where each domino has been placed? You may find the check grid useful – crossing off each domino as you find it. To give you a start, 3*5 has been marked in.

```
1  3  6  2  4  0  5  6
5  2  0  2  1  1  0  2
4  4  0  2  4  6  0  3
5  0  6  5  6  3  5  5
2  3  0  4  1  4  5  0
1  6  6  6  2  1  3  1
1  2  3  4  4  5  3  3
```

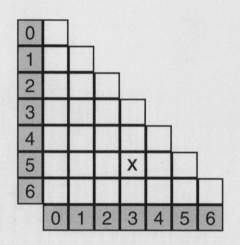

275 COG-ITATE ★

Can you see which three weights will rise and which two will fall when the man pulls the rope?

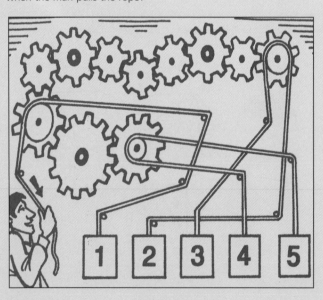

276 COG-ITATE ★

When the engineer turns the handle, will the final cog move to touch pyramid 1 or pyramid 2?

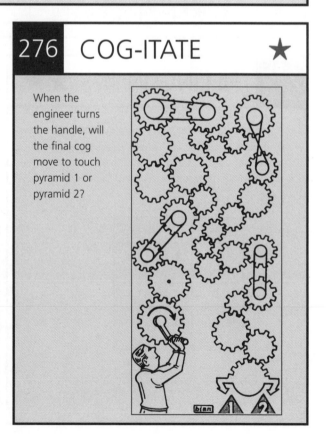

277 SWINE LINES ★

Draw three straight lines from edge to edge to divide the rectangle into five parts, each containing two pigs.

279 THREE BY FOUR ★

Only three of the figures appear in all four rectangles – which ones are they?

278 WASHDAY BLUES ★

Which of the four numbered ends is the end of the washing-line?

280 FLAG DAY ★

Arthur's flag is the same shape as Ben's, and his flag-pole is the same as Colin's but not the same as Damien's. Arthur is wearing a grey neckerchief, whilst Errol has one with stripes. Match the names to the numbers!

281 CARTWHEELS ★

Which two numbered fragments complete either wheel A or wheel B?

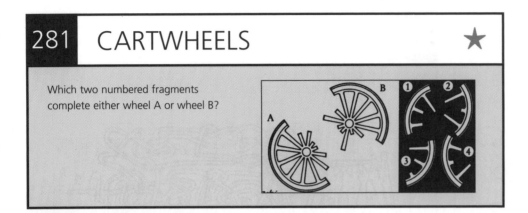

282 TSUNAMI ★★★

The numbers alongside each row or column tell you how many blocks of black squares are in a line. For example: 2, 3, 5 tells you that from left to right (or top to bottom) there is a group of two black squares, then at least one white space, then a group of three black squares, then at least one white shape, then a group of five black squares. Each block of black squares on the same line must have at least one white square between it and the next block of black squares.

Sometimes it is possible to tell which squares are going to be black without reference to other lines or columns. In the example below, we can deduce that any block of six black squares must incorporate the two central squares:

6 

Can you complete this tsunami puzzle, to reveal the hidden pattern or picture?

Column clues (left to right):

Column	Clue
1	8 13
2	2 3 2 1 1
3	2 8 1 1 3
4	1 4 2 1 12
5	1 2 1 2 5
6	4 3 2 2 5
7	2 4 2 2 4
8	2 4 1 1 3 5
9	1 4 2 1 2 5
10	1 3 2 1 3 5
11	1 6 1 3 4 5
12	4 3 6
13	2 4 1 1
14	2 9 2 1
15	1 11 4
16	1 11 3
17	1 14 5
18	1 17 2
19	4 18 4
20	2 4 12 5
21	2 22
22	1 2 22
23	1 1 1 23
24	1 3 23
25	2 4 4 18
26	2 4 4 3 8
27	1 9 4
28	1 7
29	5 4 11
30	2 4

Row clues (top to bottom):

Row	Clue
1	1 1 1 1 1
2	3 3 3 3 3 1
3	1 4 5 6 5 3
4	1 1 1 1 1
5	1 1 1 1 4 1
6	1 4 1 3 1
7	1 6 6 5 1
8	1 8 6 4
9	1 2 6 8 3
10	2 5 8 3
11	1 1 8 3
12	2 2 2 1 8 4
13	2 1 1 1 6 7
14	2 1 6 8
15	1 1 14
16	1 4 11 1
17	1 1 1 8 1
18	1 3 1 9 1
19	6 3 10 1
20	1 3 3 1 9 1
21	1 2 1 9 1
22	2 1 1 8 1
23	1 1 1 7 1
24	1 1 1 1 7 1
25	1 1 1 1 6 1
26	1 1 4 6 1
27	1 1 1 1 5
28	1 1 1 1 6 1
29	1 1 1 1 6 1
30	1 1 1 1 6 1
31	12 1 7 1
32	1 8 9
33	1 9 1 9
34	11 1 10
35	4 4 1 10

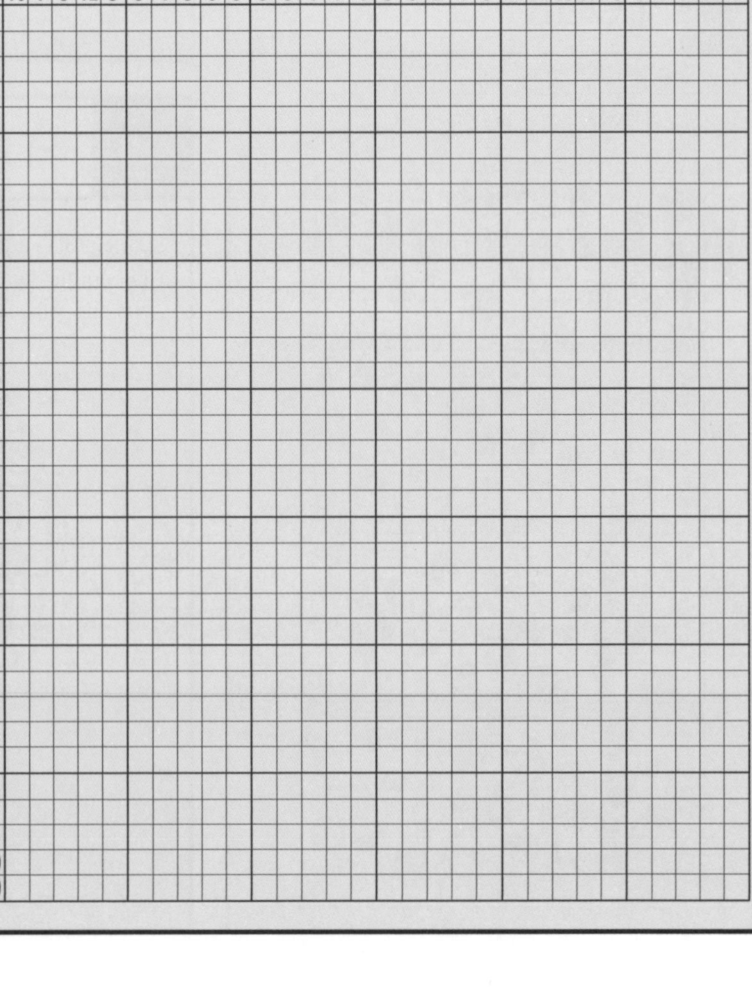

283 WIRED UP ★

Which of the four plugs should be inserted in the socket to operate the toothbrush?

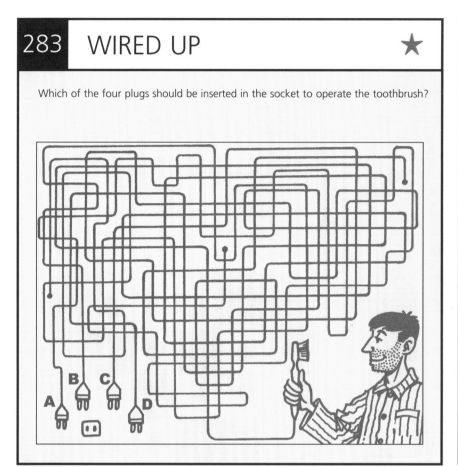

284 BLACK OUT ★

Can you see which one of the letters is shown in negative form in the top left-hand corner?

285 BALL BOY ★

Danny's mother took a photo of him with his favourite ball. Which ball in the larger picture is the same as the one in the photo?

286 FRAMED!

The top illustration shows four abstract paintings hanging in a famous art gallery. Below, we see Claud, who has bought one – but he can't remember which it was or which way up it should hang. Can you help him?

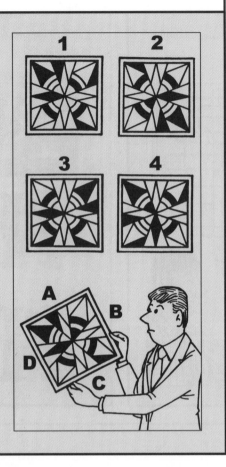

287 SYMBOLISM

Each of the four symbols represents a certain number in all the rows across – and the across totals refer to the sum of the symbols shown on that row using these numbers. Each symbol also refers to a number (it may or may not be the same number!) when used in the sums downwards, with totals at the bottom of the grid – the symbols in each column add up to the totals at the bottom, and each symbol is the same number for all the downwards sums.

Can you work out the value of the symbols shown, both horizontally and vertically?

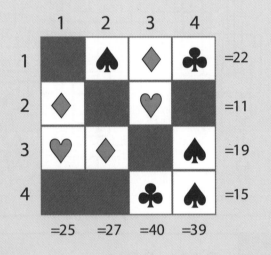

288 ABC

Each line, across and down, is to have each of the letters A, B and C, and two empty squares. The letter outside the grid shows the first or second letter in the direction of the arrow. Can you fill in the grid?

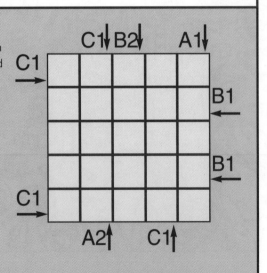

289 FILLING IN

Each of the nine empty boxes contains a different digit from 1 to 9. Each calculation is to be treated sequentially rather than according to the 'multiplication first' system. Can you fill in the empty boxes?

290 | SPOT THE DIFFERENCE

Ever since Parliament was founded politicians have enjoyed a good shout at each other! See if you can spot eight differences between the two pictures.

291 | TSUNAMI ★★★

The numbers alongside each row or column tell you how many blocks of black squares are in a line. For example: 2, 3, 5 tells you that from left to right (or top to bottom) there is a group of two black squares, then at least one white space, then a group of three black squares, then at least one white shape, then a group of five black squares. Each block of black squares on the same line must have at least one white square between it and the next block of black squares.

Sometimes it is possible to tell which squares are going to be black without reference to other lines or columns. In the example below, we can deduce that any block of six black squares must incorporate the two central squares: Can you complete this tsunami puzzle, to

6

reveal the hidden pattern or picture?

Row clues (top to bottom):

- 4 3
- 4 5
- 4 9 4
- 4 2 3 4 4
- 4 2 2 2 2 4
- 9 2 2 4 5
- 1 8 3 12
- 2 9 12
- 1 6 2 2 7
- 2 5 5
- 1 1 1
- 1 3 3 2 1 2
- 1 1 1 1 1 1 1 2 2 1
- 3 1 1 2 2 1 2
- 1 1 2 2 1
- 3 1 1 2 1
- 3 8 1 1
- 4 3 1 5 3
- 5 13 4
- 1 10 3 4
- 1 1 1 2 4 2 3
- 1 12 3 2
- 5 9 4 1
- 1 1 1 4
- 7 1 3 4
- 1 1 1 4
- 2 1 1 2 3 1 4
- 2 1 1 3 1 5
- 2 1 1 7 6
- 7 1 2 7

292 BATTLESHIPS

Do you remember the old game of battleships? This puzzle is based on that idea. Your task is to find the vessels in the diagram. Some parts of boats or sea squares have already been filled in, and a number next to a row or column refers to the number of occupied squares in that row or column. The boats may be positioned horizontally or vertically, but no two boats or parts of boats are in adjacent squares – horizontally, vertically or diagonally.

Aircraft carrier:

Battleships:

Cruisers:

Destroyers:

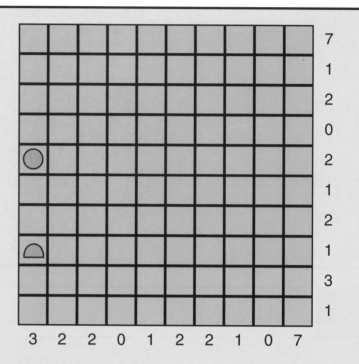

293 LOGI PATH

Use your deductive reasoning to form a pathway from the box marked START to the box marked FINISH moving in either direction horizontally or vertically (but not diagonally). The number at the beginning of every row or column indicates exactly how many boxes in that row or column your pathway must pass through. The small diagram is given as an example of how it works.

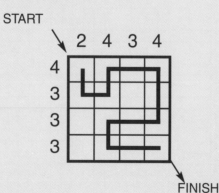

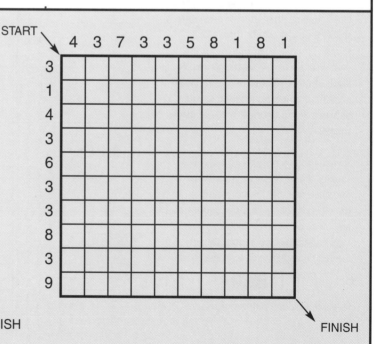

294 FOURSOME ★

The professor is looking for four identical artefacts.
Which will he choose?

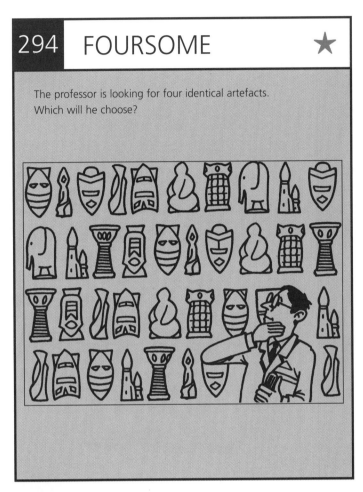

295 CAN YOU DIGIT? ★★

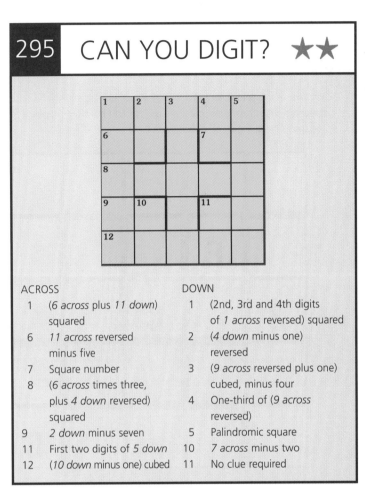

ACROSS

1 (6 across plus 11 down) squared
6 11 across reversed minus five
7 Square number
8 (6 across times three, plus 4 down reversed) squared
9 2 down minus seven
11 First two digits of 5 down
12 (10 down minus one) cubed

DOWN

1 (2nd, 3rd and 4th digits of 1 across reversed) squared
2 (4 down minus one) reversed
3 (9 across reversed plus one) cubed, minus four
4 One-third of (9 across reversed)
5 Palindromic square
10 7 across minus two
11 No clue required

296 SPOT THE DIFFERENCE ★

Can you spot ten differences between these two sledging gangs?

297 LOGI-5 ★★

Each line, across and down, is to have each of the letters A, B, C, D and E, appearing once each. Also, every shape – shown by the thick lines – must also have each of the letters in it. Can you fill in the grid?

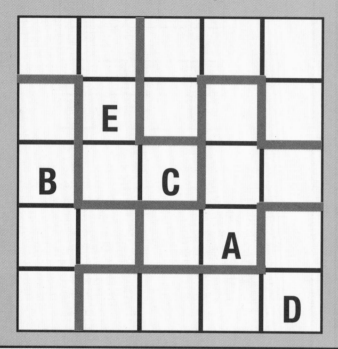

298 ON COURSE ★

Each of the lettered men must make their way along the paths to their respective destinations. Can you work out all four routes, bearing in mind that they can't use the same path and the paths must not cross?

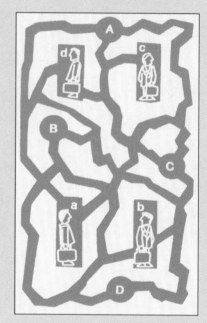

299 KNOT SO ★

Can you see which two tangles will knot and which two won't?

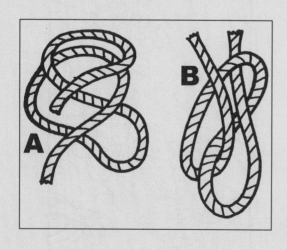

300 WASH-OUT

Each of these eight pictures is missing a detail that is present in the other seven. Can you spot all eight missing details?

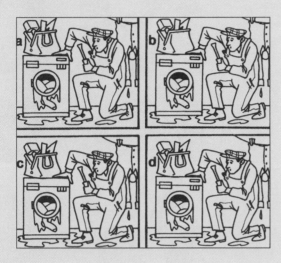
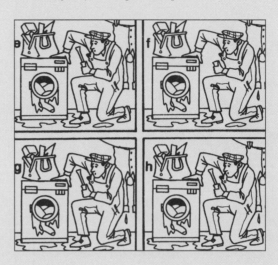

301 TSUNAMI   ★★★

The numbers alongside each row or column tell you how many blocks of black squares are in a line. For example: 2, 3, 5 tells you that from left to right (or top to bottom) there is a group of two black squares, then at least one white space, then a group of three black squares, then at least one white shape, then a group of five black squares. Each block of black squares on the same line must have at least one white square between it and the next block of black squares.

Sometimes it is possible to tell which squares are going to be black without reference to other lines or columns. In the example below, we can deduce that any block of six black squares must incorporate the two central squares:

6

Can you complete this tsunami puzzle, to reveal the hidden pattern or picture?

Row clues:
- 4 5 3 2 3 1
- 6 2 3 3 3 2
- 3 1 3 3 3 2
- 2 1 2 5 3 2
- 3 1 2 3 2 1
- 3 1 2 2 3 2 2
- 5 2 1
- 8 2 1 3
- 10 2 1 3 3
- 11 7 1 1 1 1
- 2 1 2 1 3 1 1
- 2 1 3 1 1 1 1
- 2 3 2 3 1 1 1 1 1
- 3 3 2 1 9
- 8 1 1
- 5 2 1 1 1 1 1 1
- 1 1 13
- 1 5 1 1 1 1 1 1 1 1
- 1 1 1 1 1 1 1 1 1 1 1 1
- 1 1 1 1 1 1 1 1 1 1 1 1
- 1 1 1 1
- 1 2 2 1 1
- 1 7 1 4
- 1 7 1 1 1 6
- 1 7 1 4 2
- 1 9 1 4 3
- 1 1 1 1 8
- 13 1 1 1
- 2 2 1 1
- 3 3 1 1 1 1 1 2

302 IDENTICAL TWINS ★

Two of these go-karters are identical. Which two?

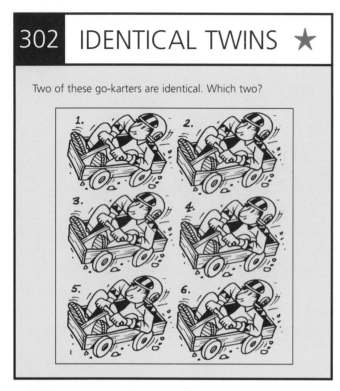

303 FIX THE PIC ★

Basher has broken all the Easter eggs. Can you put them back together again?

304 SILHOUETTE ★

Shade all the shapes which contain a dot to reveal a hidden picture.

305 TOY TRAILS ★

Ronnie has mixed up his remote control toys. Follow the lines to see which wire leads to which toy.

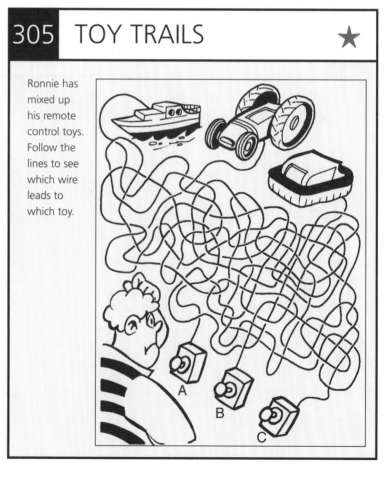

306 IN THE DEEP

Daisy the diver has lost her ring, and she can't seem to find it in the ocean. Can you find the ring, and then work your way through the maze from Daisy to it?

307 TAIL TRAILS

These three have got their kites in a tangle! Follow the lines to match them back up.

308 A KNOTTY PROBLEM

Can you decide which one of these pieces of rope will be tied into a knot when both ends are pulled?

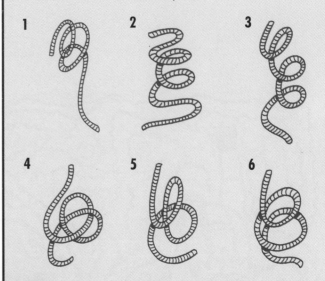

309 TRAIL SAFE

Guide the little boy home from the sweet shop by the shortest route. Make sure he doesn't bump into the bully!

310 NUMBER SQUARES

Can you find the number which will fit into the empty squares and make each equation (across and down correct)?

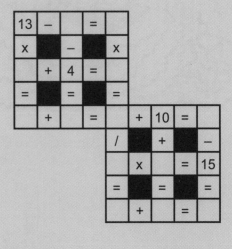

311 TSUNAMI ★★★

The numbers alongside each row or column tell you how many blocks of black squares are in a line. For example: 2, 3, 5 tells you that from left to right (or top to bottom) there is a group of two black squares, then at least one white space, then a group of three black squares, then at least one white shape, then a group of five black squares. Each block of black squares on the same line must have at least one white square between it and the next block of black squares.

Sometimes it is possible to tell which squares are going to be black without reference to other lines or columns. In the example below, we can deduce that any block of six black squares must incorporate the two central squares:

Can you complete this tsunami puzzle, to reveal the hidden pattern or picture?

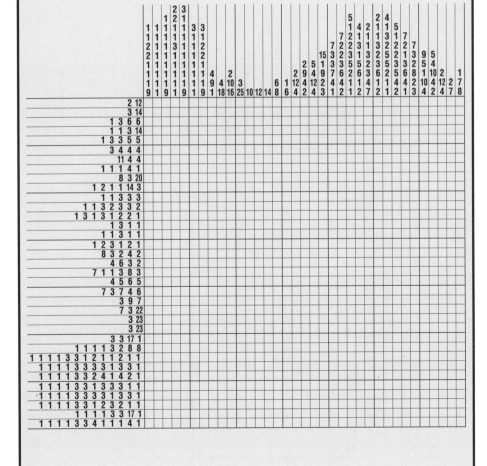

312 ABC ★★

Each line, across and down, is to have each of the letters A, B and C, and two empty squares. The letter outside the grid shows the first or second letter in the direction of the arrow. Can you fill in the grid?

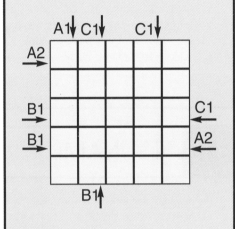

313 ABC ★★

Each line, across and down, is to have each of the letters A, B and C, and two empty squares. The letter outside the grid shows the first or second letter in the direction of the arrow. Can you fill in the grid?

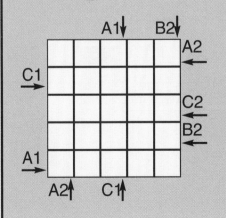

314 SQUARE NUMBERS ★★

The numbers 1–25 are entered randomly in a 5 x 5 square so that no two consecutive numbers are adjacent in any direction, or in the same row or column.
Column 1 contains four multiples of 5, but not 20, which is in the same row as 5. C3 is one lower than A2 which is four lower than B1 which is one higher than E2 which is one higher than A3 which is a prime number. B4 plus D3 equals D5; E3 plus A5, which are consecutive numbers, equals A4; C2 is an even number. B3, which is one higher than E4, is twice C4; B5 is a multiple of C5, which is not 1. 7 is in the same line diagonally as 8, and 6 is immediately below an even number, whilst 8 is below an odd number. 22 is below and diagonally adjacent to 2 which is in the same row as 14. If the long diagonal from top left to bottom right contains only one odd number, can you complete the grid?

	1	2	3	4	5
A					
B					
C					
D					
E					

315 TSUNAMI ★★

The numbers alongside each row or column tell you how many blocks of black squares are in a line. For example: 2, 3, 5 tells you that from left to right (or top to bottom) there is a group of two black squares, then at least one white space, then a group of three black squares, then at least one white shape, then a group of five black squares. Each block of black squares on the same line must have at least one white square between it and the next block of black squares.

Sometimes it is possible to tell which squares are going to be black without reference to other lines or columns. In the example below, we can deduce that any block of six black squares must incorporate the two central squares:

6 

Can you complete this tsunami puzzle, to reveal the hidden pattern or picture?

Column	Clues (top to bottom)
1	1 2 1
2	2 2 2 1
3	2 2 2 5 2
4	2 1 1 1 4
5	1 2 2 1 2 1 1
6	2 2 2 1 1 1 2
7	2 2 1 1 2 1
8	4 1 1 1 1
9	3 1 2 2 2 1
10	2 1 1 1 2 2 1 1
11	3 1 1 1 5 2
12	4 2 5 4
13	3 1 1 1 2
14	2 1 1 2
15	1 1 9
16	1 1 1 1 1
17	2 3 1 2
18	2 1 1 2 1 2
19	2 2 1 1 1
20	1 2 4 1 3

Row	Clues (left to right)
1	3
2	3 2 5 3
3	7 1 3 6
4	1 2
5	3 3 2 2 2
6	8 1 1 1 3
7	2 1 1
8	2 2 1 2 1 1
9	9 1 2
10	5 1 1
11	1 2 1
12	11 1 1
13	1 4 2 1
14	1 1 1 2 2 1 1
15	1 1 1 3 1 1 1
16	9 1 1 2
17	1 1 4
18	9 1 2
19	2 1 2 4 1
20	2 1 1 1 2 1

316 NUMBER JIG

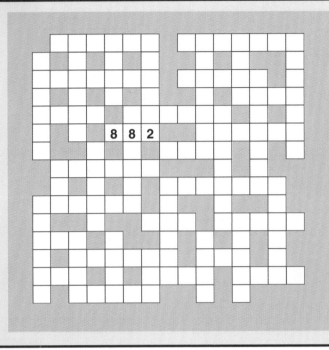

Fit the numbers into the grid as quickly as possible. One has been done for you.

3 figures	7718	450103
125	8154	485123
299	9501	510179
361		599126
420	5 figures	605544
584	19265	611683
713	28356	824916
882	34052	931152
	42166	
4 figures	61519	7 figures
1833		1385002
2985	6 figures	2439430
3772	102265	3226564
4421	176308	4748038
4506	236525	5360301
5055	251601	7243087
6909	309910	8011366

317 LOGI-PATH

Use your deductive reasoning to form a pathway from the box marked START to the box marked FINISH moving in either direction horizontally or vertically (but not diagonally). The number at the beginning of every row or column indicates exactly how many boxes in that row or column your pathway must pass through. The small diagram is given as an example of how it works.

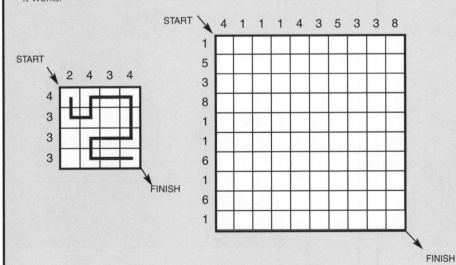

318 LOGI-5 ★★

Each line, across and down, is to have each of the letters A, B, C, D and E, appearing once each. Also, every shape – shown by the thick lines – must also have each of the letters in it. Can you fill in the grid?

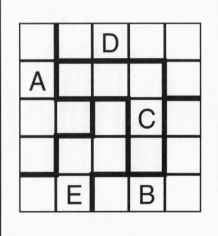

319 TELL THE UNTRUTH   ★★★

The four girls depicted in the diagram are all, I'm afraid, inveterate little liars. From the clues given below, bearing in mind that every statement they make is untrue, can you correctly name the girl in each position, work out her true age, and describe the pet she owns?

Clues

1   Jenny says, "Hello, I'm nine, and I'm sitting in position 4."
2   Josie says, "Hi, I'm sitting next to my friend whose pet is a cat."
3   Jemima says, "Hello, I'm sitting next to Julie, whose pet is a tortoise, and my friend who owns the cat is nine."
4   Julie says, "Hi, my pet is the budgie, and I'm eight years old. I'm in position 2 in the line."
5   To help you out, we'll tell you that the girl aged ten is in position 3, Josie's pet is a puppy, and the girl numbered 4 in the diagram has a budgie.

Names: Jemima; Jenny; Josie; Julie
Ages: 8; 9; 10;11
Pets: budgie; cat; puppy; tortoise

Name: —————— —————— —————— ——————

Age: —————— —————— —————— ——————

Pet: —————— —————— —————— ——————

Starting tip: Begin by identifying Julie's pet.

320 THE LONG AND WINDING TAIL   ★

Follow the tangled trail to find out which pom-pom belongs to each of my poodle pals.

FRITZY

MITZI

BITZY

A   B   C

321 IDENTICAL PAIRS   ★

Fido was really in the dog-house when he fancied a snack earlier this week! Can you find six pairs of identical squares here?

322 | TSUNAMI

The numbers alongside each row or column tell you how many blocks of black squares are in a line. For example: 2, 3, 5 tells you that from left to right (or top to bottom) there is a group of two black squares, then at least one white space, then a group of three black squares, then at least one white shape, then a group of five black squares. Each block of black squares on the same line must have at least one white square between it and the next block of black squares.

Sometimes it is possible to tell which squares are going to be black without reference to other lines or columns. In the example below, we can deduce that any block of six black squares must incorporate the two central squares:

6 ▢▢▢▢■▢▢▢▢

Can you complete this tsunami puzzle, to reveal the hidden pattern or picture?

Row clues (top to bottom):
- 16
- 9 10
- 9 5 6
- 8 5 8
- 6 6 9
- 4 6 5 5
- 6 5 6
- 5 5 8
- 5 4 9
- 2 5
- 2 5 6 5
- 2 5
- 2 5 6 4
- 2 3 1 4 1 3
- 2 5 1 6 1 3
- 1 6 1 7 1 1
- 1 2 3 1 2 4 1 1
- 1 6 1 7 1 1
- 1 6 7 1
- 1 2
- 2 1 3
- 2 2 3
- 3 3
- 1 1 5 2 1
- 4 3 4
- 3 2 7
- 2 5 5 2
- 1 2 14 3 1
- 3 3 4 3
- 3 3 4 3

---

323 | FIX THE PIC   ★

My friends are mixed-up mongrels! Match the letters and numbers to put them back together.

1   A   2   B   3   C   4   D   5   E

---

324 | FIX THE PIC   ★

Who can this shady-looking character be? Match his left side to his right side to find out his name.

325 MARY, MARTIN AND THE MAGIC MIRROR

Shade in the shapes that contain a dot to find out what's in the Magic Mirror!

326 FIX THE PIC ★

Mary and Martin are in Space today, and they've crash landed. Luckily, a friendly alien is at hand! Put the blocks on the left into the correct order to find out what it is.

327 BRAIN STRAINER ★★

Every number on an upper storey of the pyramid is the sum of the two numbers which lie under it. In this example the ⑦ must be a four, because 4+5 = 9: Begin at the base of the pyramid and climb to the top.

⑨
⑦⑤

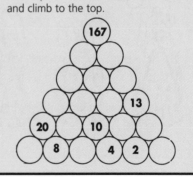

328 TSUNAMI ★★

The numbers alongside each row or column tell you how many blocks of black squares are in a line. For example: 2, 3, 5 tells you that from left to right (or top to bottom) there is a group of two black squares, then at least one white space, then a group of three black squares, then at least one white shape, then a group of five black squares. Each block of black squares on the same line must have at least one white square between it and the next block of black squares.

Sometimes it is possible to tell which squares are going to be black without reference to other lines or columns. In the example below, we can deduce that any block of six black squares must incorporate the two central squares:

6 

Can you complete this tsunami puzzle, to reveal the hidden pattern or picture?

Column clues (left to right):

Column	Clue
1	10
2	1 9
3	8 6
4	8 2 3
5	6 1 3 2
6	5 1 2
7	7 3 3
8	6 1 7
9	3 1 1 4
10	2 2 1
11	2 2 1 7
12	2 2 1 1
13	4 2 2 1
14	3 2 1 3
15	1 2 4
16	1 1 1 9
17	1 1 1 1 9
18	1 1 1 1 1 9
19	1 1 1 10
20	11

Row clues (top to bottom):

Row	Clue
1	8 1 1
2	10 1
3	6 1 1 1
4	6 1 1 1
5	6 1 1
6	3 6 1 1 1
7	2 1 3 1 1
8	2 1
9	3 1 1
10	2 1 6 1
11	1 1 1 2 1 2
12	2 1 2 1 6
13	2 1 1 6
14	2 1 5 5
15	3 1 2 1 2 5
16	3 1 2 1 5
17	3 4 1 6
18	4 2 1 7
19	6 2 1 7
20	6 2 1 7

329 SILHOUETTE ★

Shade all the shapes that contain a dot to reveal a picture.

330 DOT TO DOT ★

Something tells me this builder was reading his plans upside-down! Join the dots to complete the scene.

331   IN A FLAP   ★

Polly Parrot is very angry because she can't reach the big bag of seed that she wants for her dinner. Can you work out which path she should take to reach it?

332   IDENTICAL TWINS   ★

Which two musicians below are identical?

333 TWISTING TRAILS ★

Freddie the fisherman is in trouble. Can you lead the lifeguard to him, avoiding the perils of the sea along the way?

335 TWISTING TRAILS ★

Help Rockin' Ron find his way to the stage door so that the show can go on!

334 TSUNAMI ★★

The numbers alongside each row or column tell you how many blocks of black squares are in a line. For example: 2, 3, 5 tells you that from left to right (or top to bottom) there is a group of two black squares, then at least one white space, then a group of three black squares, then at least one white shape, then a group of five black squares. Each block of black squares on the same line must have at least one white square between it and the next block of black squares.

Sometimes it is possible to tell which squares are going to be black without reference to other lines or columns. In the example below, we can deduce that any block of six black squares must incorporate the two central squares:

6 ⬜⬜⬜⬜⬛⬜⬜⬜⬜

Can you complete this tsunami puzzle, to reveal the hidden pattern or picture?

Row clue	1,3	4,4	1,1,5,1	3,3,1,9	3,4,9	3,1,9	3,1,1,8	3,4,3,1	3,1,4,3,1	3,2,1,1,8	3,1,9	4,1,9	3,3,1,5,1	2,1,2,4	2,3
7															
9															
9															
2 2															
1 2 2 1															
2 1 1 2															
1 1 1															
2 1 2 2															
1 2 2 1															
2 2 2 2															
3 1 3															
1 3 1 3 1															
1 9 1															
7 7															
6 6															
6 6															
6 6															
5 5															
4 4															
1 7 1															

336 TSUNAMI

The numbers alongside each row or column tell you how many blocks of black squares are in a line. For example: 2, 3, 5 tells you that from left to right (or top to bottom) there is a group of two black squares, then at least one white space, then a group of three black squares, then at least one white shape, then a group of five black squares. Each block of black squares on the same line must have at least one white square between it and the next block of black squares.

Sometimes it is possible to tell which squares are going to be black without reference to other lines or columns. In the example below, we can deduce that any block of six black squares must incorporate the two central squares:

6 ☐☐☐☐■■☐☐☐☐

Can you complete this tsunami puzzle, to reveal the hidden pattern or picture?

Row clues (top to bottom):

- 4
- 4
- 1 4 2
- 1 4 1 4
- 1 3 1 4
- 3 1 1 2
- 3 4 1 1 1
- 3 4 1 1 5
- 1 1 3 2 1 4
- 3 2 2 1 3
- 3 2 1 2
- 3 1 3
- 1 1 4 4 4
- 3 18
- 3 2 4 2
- 3 1 3
- 1 1 1 1 2
- 3 2 2 1 4
- 1 1 5 2 1 4
- 5 4 1 1 1 2
- 5 2 1 1 1
- 2 2 1 1 4
- 2 2 4 1 4
- 2 2 4 1 2
- 2 2 3 4
- 3 3 4 4
- 3 3 5 2 1
- 3 4 1 1 1
- 3 4 1 1 1 1
- 2 3 13 1
- 1 3 2 1
- 3 3 2 2 4
- 5 3 2 2
- 3 3 2 2 2 2 2
- 2 1 4 2 2 2 2 2

337 DOMINO SEARCH

A standard set of dominoes has been laid out, using numbers instead of dots for clarity. Using a sharp pencil and a keen brain, can you draw in the lines to show where each domino has been placed? You may find the check grid useful – crossing off each domino as you find it.

1	6	3	6	0	6	0	2
6	2	2	6	6	5	3	1
2	4	1	2	4	4	5	0
0	5	5	3	0	4	0	3
4	1	3	1	4	5	3	3
1	5	0	0	1	6	4	2
6	2	3	2	1	4	5	5

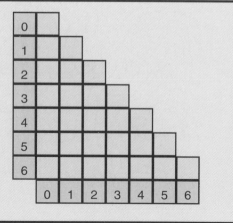

338 ABC ★★

Each line, across and down, is to have each of the letters A, B and C, and two empty squares. The letter outside the grid shows the first or second letter in the direction of the arrow. Can you fill in the grid?

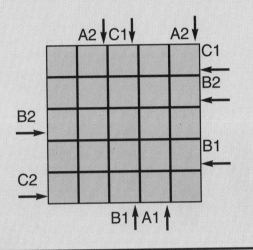

340 SWEET TOOTH ★

Here's a tricky brainteaser for you. See how quickly you can work out how many sweets each child has.

Some children are helping themselves to sweets from a jar. David takes seven more sweets than Sally, while Sally has six fewer than Tony, but twice as many as Katie. Simon has three more than Katie, who has twice as many as Philip. If Philip has two sweets, how many did the others get, and how many sweets do the children have altogether?

339 TSUNAMI ★★★

The numbers alongside each row or column tell you how many blocks of black squares are in a line. For example: 2, 3, 5 tells you that from left to right (or top to bottom) there is a group of two black squares, then at least one white space, then a group of three black squares, then at least one white shape, then a group of five black squares. Each block of black squares on the same line must have at least one white square between it and the next block of black squares.

Sometimes it is possible to tell which squares are going to be black without reference to other lines or columns. In the example below, we can deduce that any block of six black squares must incorporate the two central squares:

Can you complete this tsunami puzzle, to reveal the hidden pattern or picture?

341 LOGI-5

Each line, across and down, is to have each of the letters A, B, C, D and E, appearing once each. Also, every shape – shown by the thick lines – must also have each of the letters in it. Can you fill in the grid?

342 PILE UP

These piles of bricks aren't the random results of a child's play but clues to a final, at present blank, pile on the right. Like the rest, that one has six bricks each with a different one of the six letters. The numbers below the heaps tell you two things:

(a) The number of adjacent pairs of bricks in that column which also appear adjacent in the final pile.

(b) The number of adjacent pairs of bricks that make a correct pair but the wrong way up. So:

 would score one in the 'Correct' row if the final heap had an A directly above a C and a one in the 'Reversed' row if the final heap had a C on top of an A. From all this, can you create the final pile before it topples?

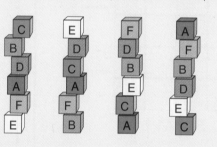 

| Correct | 0 | 0 | 0 | 1 | 5 |
| Reversed | 2 | 2 | 0 | 0 | 0 |

343 MATCH THE HALVES ★

The names of eight planets have been broken in two. Can you put them back together again?

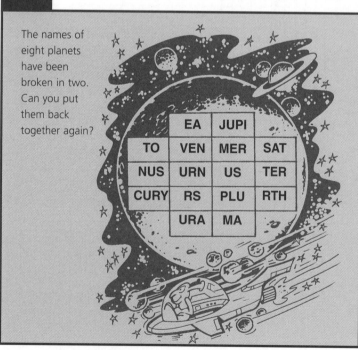

344 PICTURE PUZZLER ★

This fireman isn't sure which hose is attached to the tap, and he needs to act fast! Can you help him out?

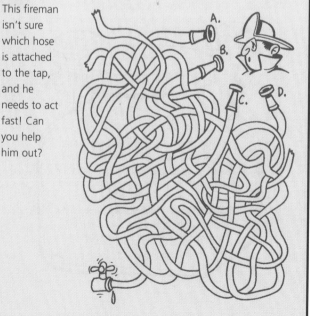

345 TSUNAMI   ★★★

The numbers alongside each row or column tell you how many blocks of black squares are in a line. For example: 2, 3, 5 tells you that from left to right (or top to bottom) there is a group of two black squares, then at least one white space, then a group of three black squares, then at least one white shape, then a group of five black squares. Each block of black squares on the same line must have at least one white square between it and the next block of black squares.

Sometimes it is possible to tell which squares are going to be black without reference to other lines or columns. In the example below, we can deduce that any block of six black squares must incorporate the two central squares:

6

Can you complete this tsunami puzzle, to reveal the hidden pattern or picture?

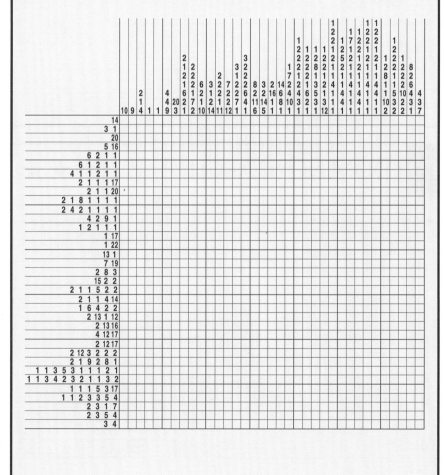

Row clues (top to bottom):

- 14
- 3 1
- 20
- 5 16
- 6 2 1 1
- 6 1 2 1 1
- 4 1 1 2 1 1
- 2 1 1 1 17
- 2 1 1 20
- 2 1 8 1 1 1 1
- 2 4 2 1 1 1 1
- 4 2 9 1
- 1 2 1 1 1
- 1 17
- 1 22
- 13 1
- 7 19
- 2 8 3
- 15 2 2
- 2 1 1 5 2 2
- 2 1 1 4 14
- 1 6 4 2 2
- 2 13 1 12
- 2 13 16
- 4 12 17
- 2 12 17
- 2 12 3 2 2 2
- 2 1 9 2 8 1
- 1 1 3 5 3 1 1 1 2 1
- 1 1 3 4 2 3 2 1 1 3 2
- 1 1 1 5 3 17
- 1 1 2 3 3 5 4
- 2 3 1 7
- 2 3 5 4
- 3 4

346 BALL GAME   ★

Can you place these cannonballs in order; from the ball nearest to the cannon to the ball furthest from the cannon?

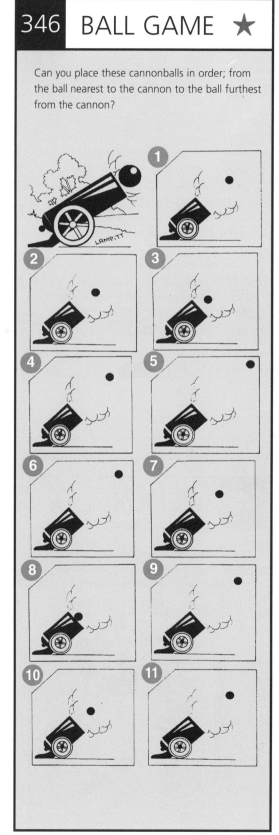

347 TSUNAMI ★★★

The numbers alongside each row or column tell you how many blocks of black squares are in a line. For example: 2, 3, 5 tells you that from left to right (or top to bottom) there is a group of two black squares, then at least one white space, then a group of three black squares, then at least one white shape, then a group of five black squares. Each block of black squares on the same line must have at least one white square between it and the next block of black squares.

Sometimes it is possible to tell which squares are going to be black without reference to other lines or columns. In the example below, we can deduce that any block of six black squares must incorporate the two central squares:

6 

Can you complete this tsunami puzzle, to reveal the hidden pattern or picture?

5 6
5 2 7 3 3
7 4 1 1
2 9 3 3
1 9
4 1 10
2 3 16
3 5 6
3 7 1
3 5 1 1 6 3 3
3 8 7
3 4 8 3 3
4 5 1 1
4 13 3 3
5 13
5 5 1 10
5 17
13 1 7
5 3 6 3 3
5 3 2
5 3 2 3 3
4 2 1
4 2 1 4
4 2 4 7
3 6 2 4 7
3 2 2 18
3 3 1 19
3 4 16 3
3 21 1 1
2 6 14 1 1
4 4 5 3
10
9
8
10

16
20
22
4 12 4
2 7 2
1 4
1 7
1 2 5
1 1 4
1 1 3
2 2 1 1 1 3
2 2 1 1 3
2 2 2 1 2
2 4 2 2 1 4
4 5 2 4 8
1 3 3 2 2 5 6
3 6 2 11
2 2 3 1 4 8
1 4 3 6 6
6 1 8 6
8 10 5
8 10 5
2 2 2 3 2 3 7
8 10 8
2 2 2 3 2 5 9
23 11
2 2 11
1 1 2 1 1 1 2 1 1 3 4
1 1 2 1 1 1 2 1 1 12
1 1 2 1 1 1 2 1 1 5 5
2 2 5 5
1 1 2 1 1 1 2 1 1 5 2 4
1 1 2 1 1 1 2 1 1 2 1
1 1 2 1 1 1 2 1 1 2 1
2 2 2 1

348 MEMORIZE ★

Study these objects carefully while someone times you for a minute, then close the book and see if you can remember them all.

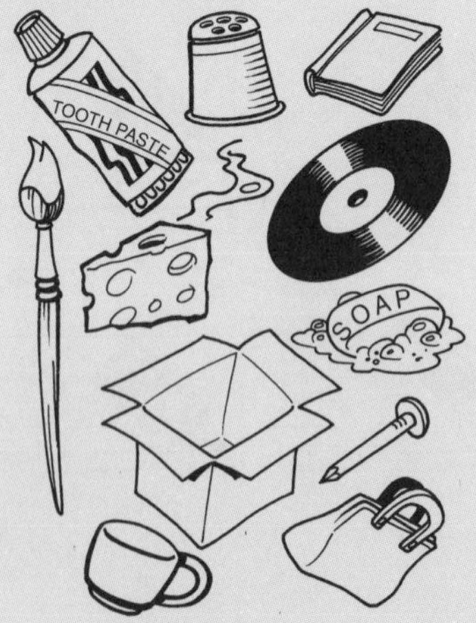

349 DOMINO SEARCH ★★

A standard set of dominoes has been laid out, using numbers instead of dots for clarity. Using a sharp pencil and a keen brain, can you draw in the lines to show where each domino has been placed? You may find the check grid useful – crossing off each domino as you find it.

1	0	3	4	5	1	2	4
6	5	0	0	0	2	3	6
3	1	6	1	2	4	4	4
6	1	5	5	0	3	3	2
6	4	0	4	5	6	3	5
5	3	2	1	3	1	0	5
6	0	1	6	2	2	2	4

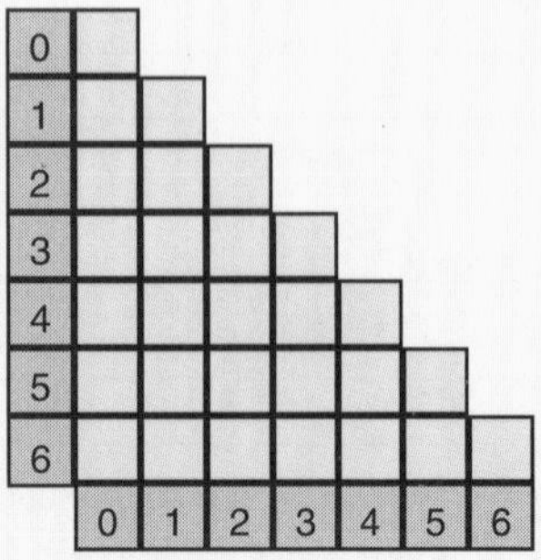

350 TIME PLEASE! ★

Look at the three clocks, then work out what the last clock should say to continue the sequence.

351 LOGI-5 ★★

Each line, across and down, is to have each of the letters A, B, C, D and E, appearing once each. Also, every shape – shown by the thick lines – must also have each of the letters in it. Can you fill in the grid?

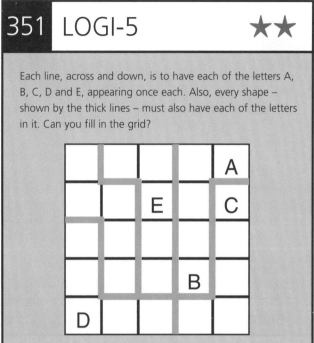

352 A BOX IN THE SHED ★★★

When Joe needed something for a job about the house, he would say "They're in a box in the shed". The four boxes shown in the diagram standing next to each other on a shelf, all of different colours, each contain a different number of useful items. From the clues given below, can you work out the full details?

Clues

1   The 43 nails of assorted sizes are not in the brown box.
2   There are 58 items in the blue box.
3   The screws are in the green box, one of whose immediate neighbours on the shelf contains the washers, and the other the largest number of items.
4   The carpet tacks are in box C.

Box colours: blue; brown; green; red
Number: 39; 43; 58; 65
Items: carpet tacks; nails; screws; washers

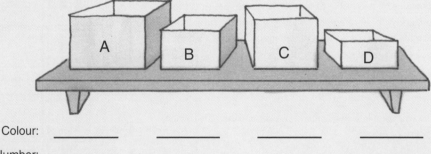

Colour: _____   _____   _____   _____

Number: _____   _____   _____   _____

Items: _____   _____   _____   _____

Starting tip: First work out the colour of the box containing the nails.

353 ALL CHANGE

At the height of Victorian England a lady of quality could only enjoy seaside bathing by hiring a bathing-machine from which she could descend modestly into the water wearing an ankle-length one-piece bathing dress. This problem features four such machines. From the clues given below, can you fully identify the lady who changed in each machine, and work out the colour of the striped bathing-costume in which she stepped into the sea?

Clues

1   Bertha's machine was immediately to the right of the one used by Miss Marchbank-

2   Machine C was the one Miss Langthorpe hired.

3   Miss Carstairs wore the green and white striped costume.

4   Euphemia Ponsonby used a machine separated from the one whose occupant wore the orange and white bathing-suit only by the one hired by Lavinia.

5   It was in machine B that one lady changed into her red and white bathing-costume.

First names: Bertha; Euphemia; Lavinia; Victoria

Surnames: Carstairs; Langthorpe; Marchbanks; Ponsonby

Costumes: blue and white; green and white; orange and white; red and white

First name: ___ ___ ___ ___

Surname: ___ ___ ___ ___

Costume: ___ ___ ___ ___

Starting tip: Start by working out the first name of the lady who hired machine D.

354 TSUNAMI

The numbers alongside each row or column tell you how many blocks of black squares are in a line. For example: 2, 3, 5 tells you that from left to right (or top to bottom) there is a group of two black squares, then at least one white space, then a group of three black squares, then at least one white shape, then a group of five black squares. Each block of black squares on the same line must have at least one white square between it and the next block of black squares.

Sometimes it is possible to tell which squares are going to be black without reference to other lines or columns. In the example below, we can deduce that any block of six black squares must incorporate the two central squares:

6 ▢▢▢▢■■▢▢▢▢

Can you complete this tsunami puzzle, to reveal the hidden pattern or picture?

Row clues
2 3
5 5
2 5 5
6 3 3
1 1 1 1 1 1
1 6 1 1 1 1 1
1 1 1 1 1 1 1 1
6 1 1 1 1
3 3 1 1 1
1 3 1 3 1 1
5 1 2 2
1 1 2 1 1
1 2 1 1 1 1 1
4 1 4 1 3
3 4 1 1 1 1 1
3 1 2 1 2 2 1
1 12
20
5 2 2
3 1 4 4

355 IN THE MAIL

Four housewife neighbours in a suburban area of an American town each had a different coloured mailbox at the entrance to her property. From the clues given below, can you work out the name of the woman who lives at each address, and work out the colour of her mailbox?

Clues

1   The green mailbox is next to Gemma's on one side, and Mrs Gerber's on the other.

2   Arlene chose the yellow mailbox for her gate, at a house with a higher number than Mrs Fishbein's.

3   The red mailbox is at Mrs Baron's house.

4   The blue mailbox is on the gate of number 232, which is not Louise's home.

First names: Arlene; Gemma; Kate; Louise
Surnames: Baron; Fishbein; Flint; Gerber
Mailboxes: blue; green; red; yellow

Starting tip: Begin by placing the green mailbox.

228   230   232   234

First name: _____ _____ _____ _____

Surname: _____ _____ _____ _____

Colour: _____ _____ _____ _____

356 LOGISTICAL

Unfortunately, the Driving Test Centre had to fail five drivers this morning. From the following information, can you discover the time of each candidate's test, the botched manoeuvre that contributed most to each failure, and where that manoeuvre took place?

Clues

1   Helen Weales messed up her reversing, while Ron Gear came to grief in Hawthorn Way.

2   Roland Brake's test was at 9 o'clock, but his examiner didn't take him along Mill Road.

3   Rex Chance's test was an hour before that of the candidate who made a poor manoeuvre in Market Street, while Vera Swerve's test began half an hour after the one that was failed on the emergency stop.

4   The test failed on the parking manoeuvre began at 10.30.

5   The 9.30 candidate made a mistake in Balmoral Close, and the failed hill start was halfway up Church Hill.

	Roland Brake	Rex Chance	Ron Gear	Vera Swerve	Helen Weales	Emergency stop	Hill start	Parking	Reversing	Signalling	Balmoral Close	Church Hill	Hawthorn Way	Market Street	Mill Road
9.00															
9.30															
10.30															
11.00															
11.30															
Balmoral Close															
Church Hill															
Hawthorn Way															
Market Street															
Mill Road															
Emergency stop															
Hill start															
Parking															
Reversing															
Signalling															

Time	Candidate	Manoeuvre	Location

Record in this grid all the information obtained from the clues, by using a cross to indicate a definite "no" and a tick to show a definite "yes". Transfer these to all sections of the grid thus eliminating all but one possibility, which must be the correct one.

357 SPACE TRAILS ★

This astronaut seems to have lost her way! Can you guide her safely back to her spaceship?

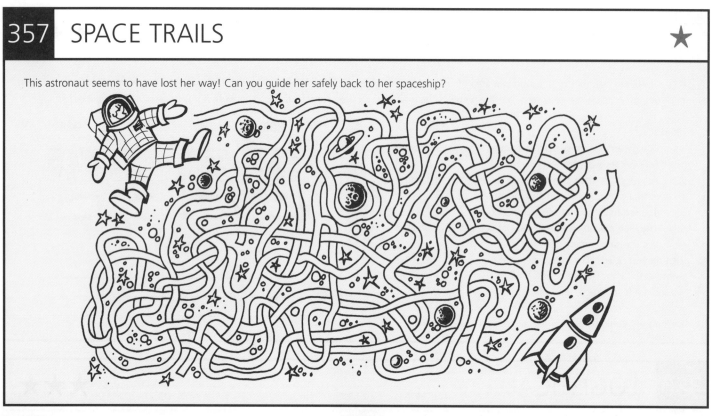

358 SMART ALEC ★

Smart Alec has invented a teddy-bear making machine. Which two teddies are identical?

359 IDENTICAL PAIRS ★

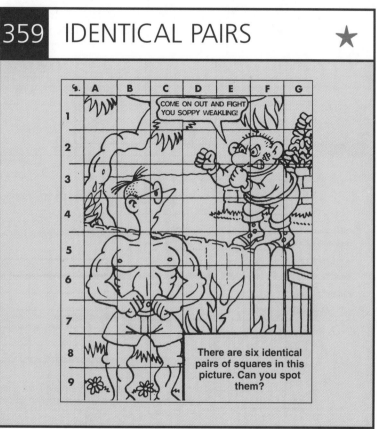

COME ON OUT AND FIGHT YOU SOPPY WEAKLING!

There are six identical pairs of squares in this picture. Can you spot them?

360 TSUNAMI ★★

The numbers alongside each row or column tell you how many blocks of black squares are in a line. For example: 2, 3, 5 tells you that from left to right (or top to bottom) there is a group of two black squares, then at least one white space, then a group of three black squares, then at least one white shape, then a group of five black squares. Each block of black squares on the same line must have at least one white square between it and the next block of black squares.

Sometimes it is possible to tell which squares are going to be black without reference to other lines or columns. In the example below, we can deduce that any block of six black squares must incorporate the two central squares:

6

Can you complete this tsunami puzzle, to reveal the hidden pattern or picture?

Column clues (left to right), top to bottom per column:

							1	1										5	
		1	5	2	1 4	1 2											5		
	1	1	2	2	4	2											2		
	1	5	2	2	3	3	4	11	12	10	6	3	4	7	3	5	5	6	
11	1	11	1	3	3	2	3	8	2	2	2	2	8	7	4	2	2	2	2

Row clues (top to bottom):

- 1 1 1 1 1 1
- 1 1 1 5
- 1 1 1 1 1 5
- 5 3 7
- 1 1 1 1 3 3 3
- 1 1 6 3 2
- 1 1 3 3 2
- 4 2 5 2
- 1 1 7 4
- 1 1 1 11
- 1 1 1 10 1
- 11 1
- 2 8
- 1 4 2
- 2 2 2 2
- 1 1 2
- 2 1 2
- 2 1 1
- 1 1
- 1 1

---

361 LOGI-5 ★★

Each line, across and down, is to have each of the letters A, B, C, D and E, appearing once each. Also, every shape – shown by the thick lines – must also have each of the letters in it. Can you fill in the grid?

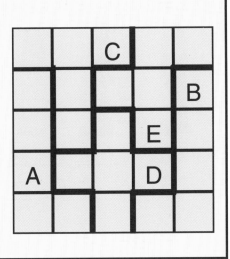

---

362 FILLING IN ★★

Each of the nine empty boxes contains a different digit from 1 to 9. Each calculation is to be treated sequentially rather than according to the 'multiplication first' system. Can you fill in the empty boxes?

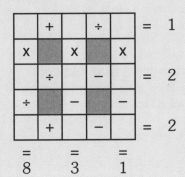

363 | STAMPS OF VALUE

A new set of stamps has just been issued in Philatelia, and four of the values are shown here. From the clues given below, can you work out the design on each stamp, its face value, and the colour in which its frame and figures of value are printed?

Clues

1   The figure 5 does not appear in brown on any of the four stamps.
2   The stamp depicting the cathedral, which has a zero in its value panel, is shown immediately to the right of the stamp with a brown frame.
3   Stamp 4 has a 1 in its value panel, while the harbour is not the design featured on stamp 3.
4   The 15 cents stamp is shown in a position directly above or below the blue one.
5   The stamp with the red frame bears the next highest value to that depicting the mountains, which is not in position 1.

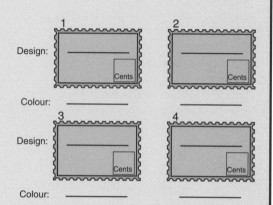

Designs: cathedral; harbour; mountains; waterfall
Values: 10 cents; 15 cents; 25 cents; 50 cents
Colours: blue; brown; green; red

Starting tip: Begin by working out the value on the brown stamp.

364 | SNACK TIME

As Tommy walked down the street he met in fairly quick succession four of his friends, each of whom was eating something different. As it was a rather chilly day, each lad was wearing a sweater. From the clues given below, can you name each of the boys numbered 1 to 4 in the diagram in the order in which they were met, and say what coloured sweater each was wearing and what item each was eating?

Clues

1   Tommy met Kevin, who was wearing the blue sweater, some time later than`he came across the lad who was eating a lollipop.
2   The boy in the beige sweater was the third friend Tommy met.
3   The youth eating a banana, who was not Simon, was encountered next after the one wearing the green sweater.
4   The lad in the red sweater, who was not Danny, was encountered some time after Lewis, whose snack was the chocolate bar.

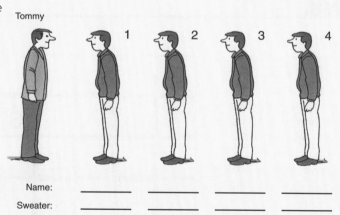

Names: Danny; Kevin; Lewis; Simon
Sweaters: beige; blue; green; red
Snacks: apple; banana; chocolate bar; lollipop

Starting tip: First name the boy in the red sweater.

365 LOGISTICAL ★★★

Five men have been employed in different capacities at the airport for varying lengths of time. What is each man's full name, what does he do and for how many years has he worked at the airport?

Clues

1 The baggage handler joined the airport staff six years ago.
2 The electrician's period of service is longer than Ledger's.
3 It is five years since Quentin started work at the airport.
4 The traffic controller has worked there longer than Denzil, but not as long as Marshall.
5 Forrest has not been employed at the airport for as long as Banks.
6 Matthew enjoys his job as an airport security guard.
7 Lawrence Adamson has not worked at the airport for as long as the man whose voice is regularly heard on the public address system.

	Adamson	Banks	Forrest	Ledger	Marshall	Announcer	Baggage handler	Electrician	Security guard	Traffic controller	4 years	5 years	6 years	7 years	8 years
Benedict															
Denzil															
Lawrence															
Matthew															
Quentin															
4 years															
5 years															
6 years															
7 years															
8 years															
Announcer															
Baggage handler															
Electrician															
Security guard															
Traffic controller															

Record in this grid all the information obtained from the clues, by using a cross to indicate a definite "no" and a tick to show a definite "yes". Transfer these to all sections of the grid thus eliminating all but one possibility, which must be the correct one.

Forename	Surname	Job	Length of service

366 SPOT THE DIFFERENCES ★

Can you spot eight differences between these two pictures of carol singers?

367 GOAL GETTER ★

Follow the correct path to help Sport score a goal!

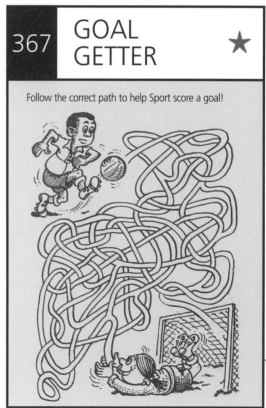

368 TSUNAMI ★★★

The numbers alongside each row or column tell you how many blocks of black squares are in a line. For example: 2, 3, 5 tells you that from left to right (or top to bottom) there is a group of two black squares, then at least one white space, then a group of three black squares, then at least one white shape, then a group of five black squares. Each block of black squares on the same line must have at least one white square between it and the next block of black squares.

Sometimes it is possible to tell which squares are going to be black without reference to other lines or columns. In the example below, we can deduce that any block of six black squares must incorporate the two central squares:

6

Can you complete this tsunami puzzle, to reveal the hidden pattern or picture?

Row clues (top to bottom):
- 5
- 1 9 1
- 1 1 6 3 1 1
- 1 3 3 3 1
- 3 5 2
- 2 7 2
- 1 1 3 5
- 1 1 2 4 1
- 1 4 2 1 1 1
- 3 3 1
- 4 2 2 4
- 5 5
- 4 1 2 2 7
- 2 2 1 5
- 6 2 3
- 3 1 3 5
- 4 1 4
- 2 2
- 1 7 2 2
- 1 1 2 1 1 3 2
- 1 2 1 2 1
- 3 3 1 1
- 3 2 3 1 1 1
- 5 1 1 1 1 1 1
- 8 1 2 1 3
- 1 7 1 4 1
- 1 2 3 1 3 4 1
- 1 2 1 2 1 3 2
- 5 3 2 2 2
- 3 6 3 1 1
- 3 4 5 1 1 1
- 4 2 1 4 2 2 1
- 3 3 10 3
- 1 2 6 6 2 1
- 3 5 1 5 1 1

369 SNAPSHOTS ★

These holiday snaps are in a muddle! Can you put them in the right order from the sun just coming over the horizon, to its highest point in the sky?

370 A MAZING ★

Untangle the lines to see who each musical instrument belongs to.

Tom   Dick   Harry

371 TSUNAMI ★★★

The numbers alongside each row or column tell you how many blocks of black squares are in a line. For example: 2, 3, 5 tells you that from left to right (or top to bottom) there is a group of two black squares, then at least one white space, then a group of three black squares, then at least one white shape, then a group of five black squares. Each block of black squares on the same line must have at least one white square between it and the next block of black squares.

Sometimes it is possible to tell which squares are going to be black without reference to other lines or columns. In the example below, we can deduce that any block of six black squares must incorporate the two central squares:

Can you complete this tsunami puzzle, to reveal the hidden pattern or picture?

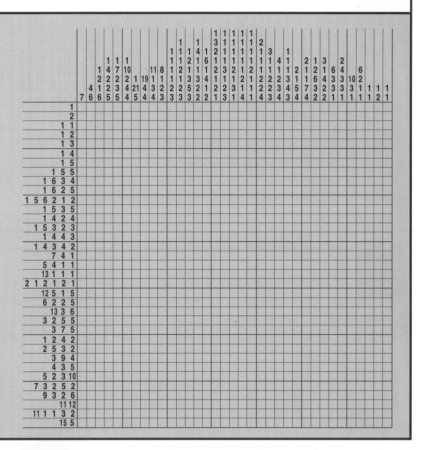

372 TROUBLESOME TRIANGLE ★★

The numbers 1–15 are to be inserted into the grid. No two consecutive numbers are in the same row, arrowed diagonal or diagonally adjacent box. The numbers on the left show the total in the horizontal row and those below show the total of the diagonal. Given that the numbers in the right-hand diagonal totalling 34 are all odd numbers, can you complete the grid?

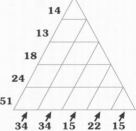

14
13
18
24
51
34 34 15 22 15

373 BATTLESHIPS ★★

Do you remember the old game of battleships? This puzzle is based on that idea. Your task is to find the vessels in the diagram. Some parts of boats or sea squares have already been filled in, and a number next to a row or column refers to the number of occupied squares in that row or column. The boats may be positioned horizontally or vertically, but no two boats or parts of boats are in adjacent squares – horizontally, vertically or diagonally.

Aircraft carrier:
Battleships:
Cruisers:
Destroyers:

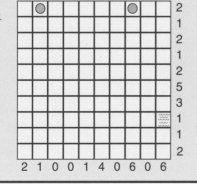

2 1 0 0 1 4 0 6 0 6

2
1
2
2
1
2
5
3
1
1
2

374 LOGI-PATH ★★

Use your deductive reasoning to form a pathway from the box marked START to the box marked FINISH moving in either direction horizontally or vertically (but not diagonally). The number at the beginning of every row or column indicates exactly how many boxes in that row or column your pathway must pass through. The small diagram is given as an example of how it works.

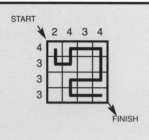

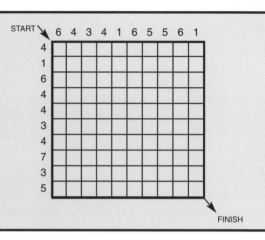

375 VILLAGE VIEWS ★★

Three friends who were artists each produced a work showing a different feature of the village they all lived in. From the clues given below, can you identify the three, say which view each chose to depict, and work out the medium in which each worked?

Clues

1 Ms Frame chose the village church as her subject.

2 Rosalind, whose surname is not Canvass, produced the oil painting.

3 The windmill was the subject of the watercolour painting, which was not the work of Nadine.

4 The pond was not the view selected by the artist who favoured pen and ink for her picture.

First name	Surname	View	Medium

	Canvass	Frame	Pallett	Pond	Village church	Windmill	Oils	Pen and ink	Watercolour
Josephine									
Nadine									
Rosalind									
Oils									
Pen and ink									
Watercolour									
Pond									
Village church									
Windmill									

376 LOGI-PATH ★★

Use your deductive reasoning to form a pathway from the box marked START to the box marked FINISH moving in either direction horizontally or vertically (but not diagonally). The number at the beginning of every row or column indicates exactly how many boxes in that row or column your pathway must pass through. The small diagram is given as an example of how it works.

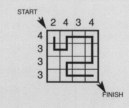

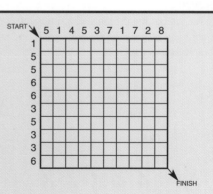

377 TSUNAMI ★★

The numbers alongside each row or column tell you how many blocks of black squares are in a line. For example: 2, 3, 5 tells you that from left to right (or top to bottom) there is a group of two black squares, then at least one white space, then a group of three black squares, then at least one white shape, then a group of five black squares. Each block of black squares on the same line must have at least one white square between it and the next block of black squares.

Sometimes it is possible to tell which squares are going to be black without reference to other lines or columns. In the example below, we can deduce that any block of six black squares must incorporate the two central squares:

6

Can you complete this tsunami puzzle, to reveal the hidden pattern or picture?

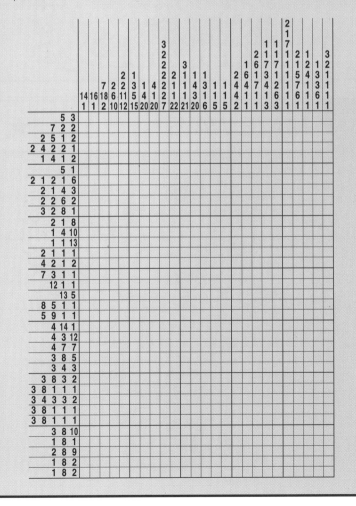

378 MIX 'N' MATCH ★

These chaps are having a bad day!
Match the correct halves to remake them.

379 PICTURE PUZZLER ★

Can you help Roberto find his violin bow? Work out which bow is at the bottom of the pile.

380 TRAIL TALE

Humphrey Hunter has gone off looking for the disgusting Slop Monster, which turns its victims to slime when it catches them. Humph needs ten bullets to defend himself. Can you find them all in the picture.

382 FILLING IN ★★

Each of the nine empty boxes contains a different digit from 1 to 9. Each calculation is to be treated sequentially rather than according to the 'multiplication first' system. Can you fill in the empty boxes?

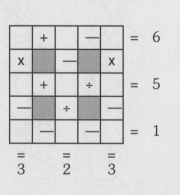

381 ON THE TRAIL ★

Follow the vines to see what Sue's trying to find!

383 MAZE WAYS ★

How does the photographer reach the rare rhinopotomus without crossing any lines?

384 TSUNAMI ★★★

The numbers alongside each row or column tell you how many blocks of black squares are in a line. For example: 2, 3, 5 tells you that from left to right (or top to bottom) there is a group of two black squares, then at least one white space, then a group of three black squares, then at least one white shape, then a group of five black squares. Each block of black squares on the same line must have at least one white square between it and the next block of black squares.

Sometimes it is possible to tell which squares are going to be black without reference to other lines or columns. In the example below, we can deduce that any block of six black squares must incorporate the two central squares:

Can you complete this tsunami puzzle, to reveal the hidden pattern or picture?

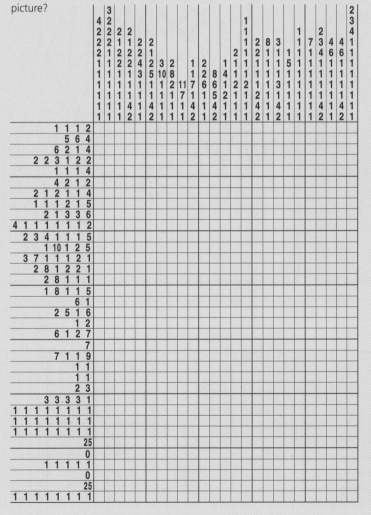

385 SQUARE PAIRS ★

In this picture there are six pairs of identical squares. Can you find them?

386 HIDE 'N' SEEK ★

Now look very hard at the spotty picture above and see if you can shade in the animal. When you've done that try and guess which moth won't be eaten by the bird when it lands on the tree....
IT'S ALL CAMOUFLAGE!

387 | TWIT TWOO ★

Olly the owl and his five brothers, Oswald, Oscar, Owen, Orinoco and Traffic (he was called traffic because he wouldn't stop hooting) are hanging around on a branch. Olly and Oscar are identical twins. Can you spot them?

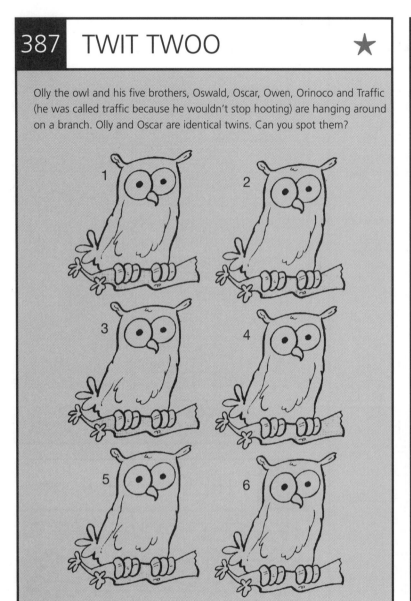

388 | SILHOUETTE ★

Shade every shape that contains a dot to reveal a scary creature.

389 | CAN YOU DIGIT ★★

ACROSS

1   (6 across plus 11 down) squared
6   11 across reversed minus five
7   Square number
8   (6 across times three, plus 4 down reversed) squared
9   2 down minus seven
11 First two digits of 5 down
12 (10 down minus one) cubed

DOWN

1   (2nd, 3rd and 4th digits of 1 across reversed) squared
2   (4 down minus one) reversed
3   (9 across reversed plus one) cubed, minus four
4   One-third of (9 across reversed)
5   Palindromic square
10 7 across minus two
11 No clue required

1	2	3	4	5
6			7	
8				
9	10		11	
12				

390 | ON THE SHELF

The young professor is trying to sort out the shelves in his lab. Can you help him by working out which three objects only appear once? A good way to start would be to colour the picture in, giving things that appear more than once the same colour.

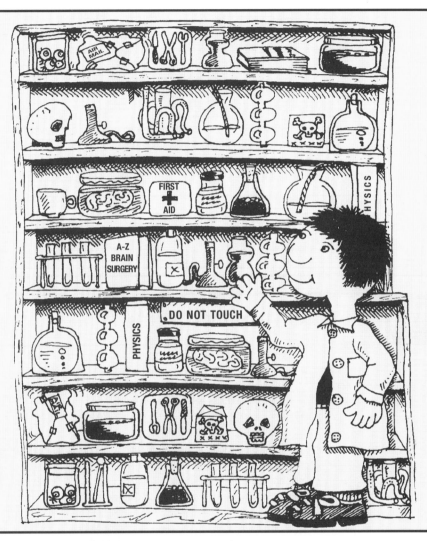

391 | MATCH UP ★

Can you see which two small rectangles contain the same four symbols?

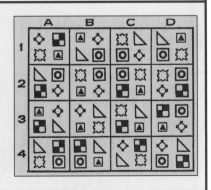

392 | SQUARE BASHING ★★

A square has sides of equal length. How many squares of all sizes are more red than green?

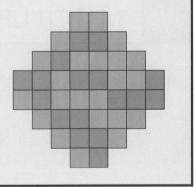

393 STAR STUDENTS

In a magazine article, three popular Albion-TV personalities talk about their time at university, studying for careers which they never pursued after getting into television. From the clues given below, can you work out each woman's full name, what she does on Albion-TV and what she trained to be originally?

Clues

1 It wasn't Donna who was trained as a teacher.
2 Miss Knight is host of Albion-TV's popular Saturday evening quiz show Go For It!
3 Laura is a newsreader, presenting Albion-TV's flagship 9.00pm summary every weekday.
4 Susan Niven never had any ambition to be a nurse.
5 It isn't the one-time student teacher who now presents current affairs programmes for Albion-TV.

First name	Surname	TV career	Studied as

	Knight	Niven	Robins	Newsreader	Presenter	Quiz host	Nurse	Solicitor	Teacher
Donna									
Laura									
Susan									
Nurse									
Solicitor									
Teacher									
Newsreader									
Presenter									
Quiz host									

394 GIVING IT SOME WELLY

Four lads were fishing for tiddlers in a shallow stream, each wearing a different coloured pair of wellington boots. From the clues given below, can you identify the boys in positions 1 to 4, and work out the colour of the boots each was wearing?

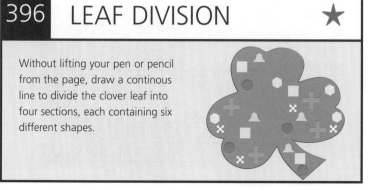

Clues

1 The lad in the red boots is somewhere to the left of Shaun, whose surname is not Brook.
2 Darren Poole is somewhere to the right of the youth in the brown boots.
3 Wader number 3 is Johnny, but the surname of the lad in position 2 is not Burne.
4 The green boots are worn by a lad wading alongside Garry, while Waters is standing next to his friend whose boots are black.

First names: Darren; Garry; Johnny; Shaun
Surnames: Brook; Burne; Poole; Waters
Boots: black; brown; green; red

First Name: _____ _____ _____ _____
Surname: _____ _____ _____ _____
Boots: _____ _____ _____ _____

Starting tip: Start by working out the first name of the lad in position 1.

395 MATCH UP ★★

Can you see which two small rectangles contain the same four symbols?

396 LEAF DIVISION ★

Without lifting your pen or pencil from the page, draw a continous line to divide the clover leaf into four sections, each containing six different shapes.

397 | BATTLESHIPS

Do you remember the old game of battleships? This puzzle is based on that idea. Your task is to find the vessels in the diagram. Some parts of boats or sea squares have already been filled in, and a number next to a row or column refers to the number of occupied squares in that row or column. The boats may be positioned horizontally or vertically, but no two boats or parts of boats are in adjacent squares – horizontally, vertically or diagonally.

Aircraft carrier:

Battleships:

Cruisers:

Destroyers:

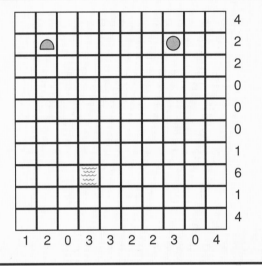

Row totals (top to bottom): 4, 2, 2, 0, 0, 0, 1, 6, 1, 4

Column totals (left to right): 1 2 0 3 3 2 2 3 0 4

398 | THAT LITTLE BIT OF DIFFERENCE ★

There are eight differences between the two cartoons. Can you spot them?

399 | COLOURFUL CONUNDRUM ★

These ten colour sequences (each of five boxes) can be fitted crossword-fashion into the grid below, so that all are placed either 'Across' or 'Down'. One colour is already in position, to get you off to a good start.

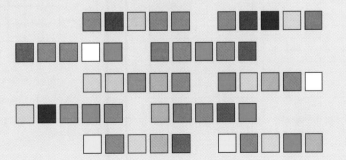

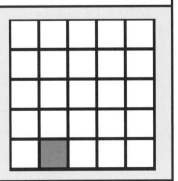

400 TSUNAMI

The numbers alongside each row or column tell you how many blocks of black squares are in a line. For example: 2, 3, 5 tells you that from left to right (or top to bottom) there is a group of two black squares, then at least one white space, then a group of three black squares, then at least one white shape, then a group of five black squares. Each block of black squares on the same line must have at least one white square between it and the next block of black squares.

Sometimes it is possible to tell which squares are going to be black without reference to other lines or columns. In the example below, we can deduce that any block of six black squares must incorporate the two central squares:

Can you complete this tsunami puzzle, to reveal the hidden pattern or picture?

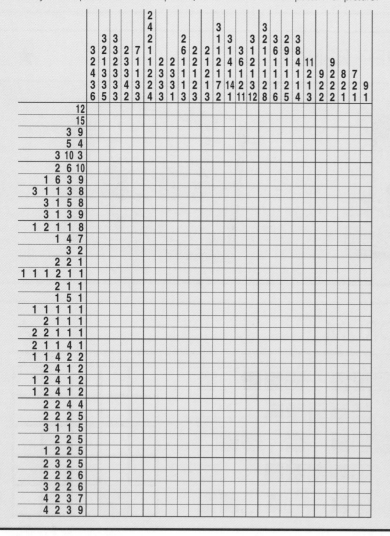

401 ENSIGN

Starting from 9, find one way by which – if you insert all four arithmetical signs (two of them twice) in the blank squares and carry out all the operations in sequence – you can obtain the answer 6 (as shown).

402 BATTLESHIPS ★★

Do you remember the old game of battleships? This puzzle is based on that idea. Your task is to find the vessels in the diagram. Some parts of boats or sea squares have already been filled in, and a number next to a row or column refers to the number of occupied squares in that row or column. The boats may be positioned horizontally or vertically, but no two boats or parts of boats are in adjacent squares – horizontally, vertically or diagonally.

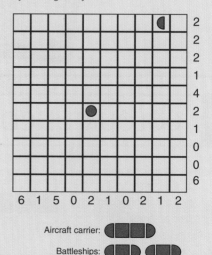

403 ZEROING IN ★

Twenty of the twenty-five squares in the diagram each contain a different one of the numbers 1 to 20, while each of the other five squares contains a zero. From the clues given below, can you place the correct number in each square? NB Where the phrase 'number' or 'single-digit number' occurs in a clue, this does not include zeros.

Clues

1 No row, column or diagonal (long or short) contains more than one zero.
2 The 19 in square B3 is the only two-digit number in that row, while the 7 is the only single-digit number in row 2.
3 The 9 is immediately below the 16, and immediately left of the 12.
4 The numbers in column E total 45, and those in row 2 total 51.
5 The number in A4 is five higher than the one in E5, which is itself one higher than the one in C2.
6 The 11 is immediately to the right of the 5 in row 4, while the 2 is to be found in a higher row than the 4.
7 The 17 appears in column D, somewhere below a zero, and somewhere above the 8.
8 The four numbers in column C are all even numbers, but do not include the 18.
9 The number 1 can be found in row 5, and the 6 in row 1.
10 The 10 is in the same column as the 3, but higher up.

Starting tip; Begin by placing the 9.

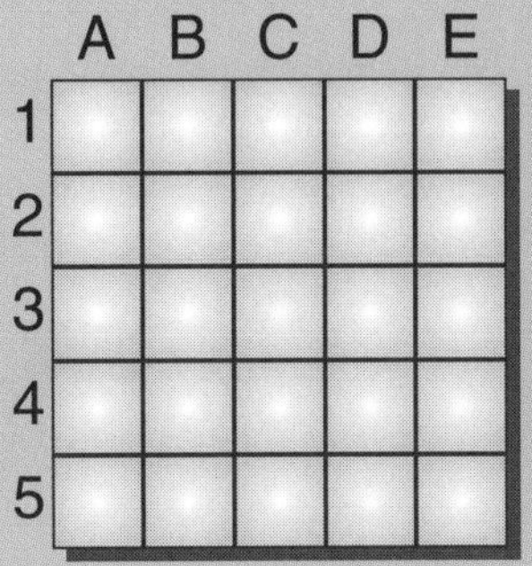
A B C D E
1
2
3
4
5

404 TSUNAMI ★★★

The numbers alongside each row or column tell you how many blocks of black squares are in a line. For example: 2, 3, 5 tells you that from left to right (or top to bottom) there is a group of two black squares, then at least one white space, then a group of three black squares, then at least one white shape, then a group of five black squares. Each block of black squares on the same line must have at least one white square between it and the next block of black squares.

Sometimes it is possible to tell which squares are going to be black without reference to other lines or columns. In the example below, we can deduce that any block of six black squares must incorporate the two central squares:

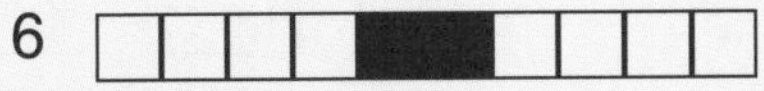
6

Can you complete this tsunami puzzle, to reveal the hidden pattern or picture?

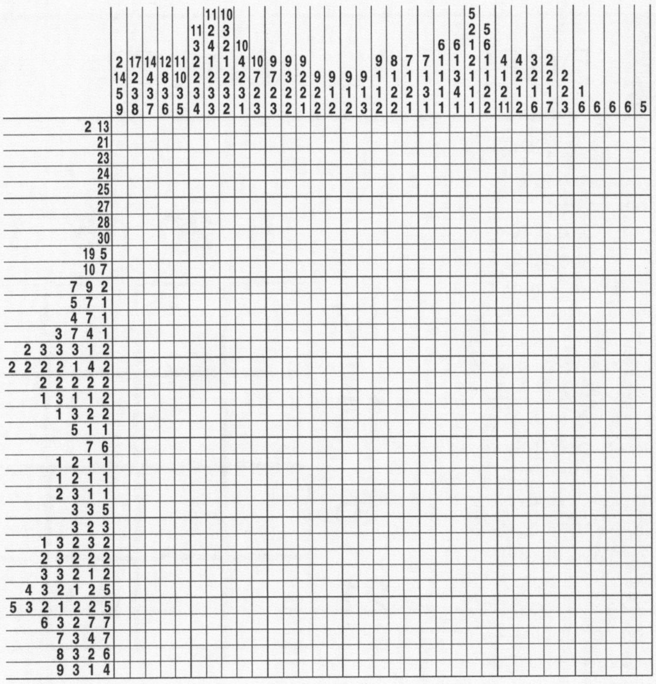
2 14 5 9
17 2 3 8
14 4 3 7
12 8 3 6
11 10 3 5
11 3 2 2 3 4
11 2 4 1 2 3 3
10 3 2 1 2 3 2
10 4 2 3 1
10 7 2 3
9 7 2 3
9 3 2 2
9 2 2 1
9 2 2
9 1 2
9 1 2
9 1 3
9 1 1 2
8 1 2 2
7 1 2 1
7 1 3 1
6 1 1 1 1
6 1 3 4 1
5 2 1 2 1 1 1
5 6 1 1 2 2
4 1 2 11
4 2 1 2
3 2 1 6
2 2 1 7
2 2 3
1 6
6
6
6
5
2 13
21
23
24
25
27
28
30
19 5
10 7
7 9 2
5 7 1
4 7 1
3 7 4 1
2 3 3 3 1 2
2 2 2 2 1 4 2
2 2 2 2 2
1 3 1 1 2
1 3 2 2
5 1 1
7 6
1 2 1 1
1 2 1 1
2 3 1 1
3 3 5
3 2 3
1 3 2 3 2
2 3 2 2 2
3 3 2 1 2
4 3 2 1 2 5
5 3 2 1 2 2 5
6 3 2 7 7
7 3 4 7
8 3 2 6
9 3 1 4

405 TSUNAMI ★★★

The numbers alongside each row or column tell you how many blocks of black squares are in a line. For example: 2, 3, 5 tells you that from left to right (or top to bottom) there is a group of two black squares, then at least one white space, then a group of three black squares, then at least one white shape, then a group of five black squares. Each block of black squares on the same line must have at least one white square between it and the next block of black squares.

Sometimes it is possible to tell which squares are going to be black without reference to other lines or columns. In the example below, we can deduce that any block of six black squares must incorporate the two central squares:

6

Can you complete this tsunami puzzle, to reveal the hidden pattern or picture?

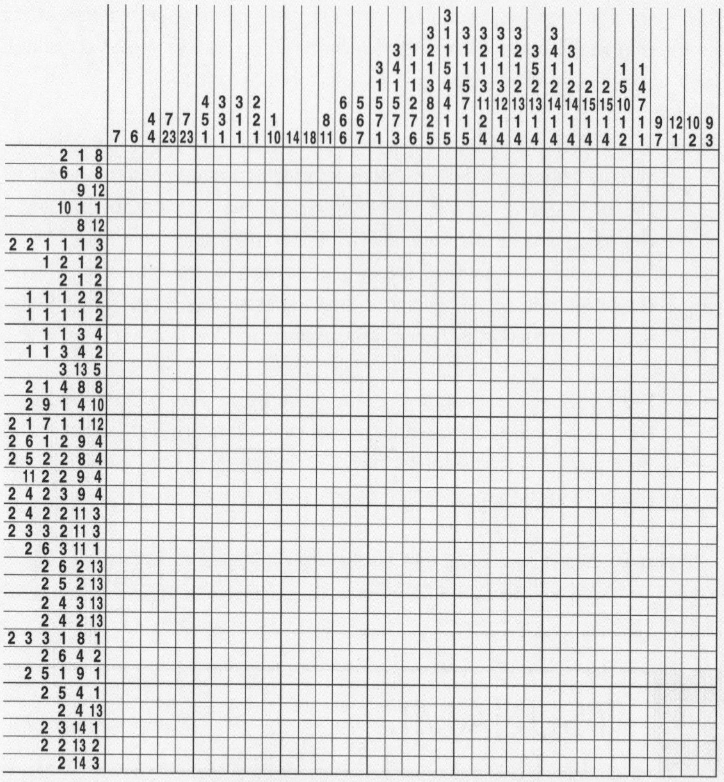
7
6
4 4
7 23
7 23
4 5 1
3 3 1
3 1 1
2 2 1
1 10
14
18
8 11
6 6 6
5 6 7
3 1 5 7 1
3 4 1 5 7 3
1 1 1 2 7 6
3 2 1 3 8 2 5
3 1 1 5 4 4 1 5
3 1 1 5 7 1 5
3 2 1 3 11 2 4
3 1 1 3 12 1 4
3 2 1 2 13 1 4
3 5 2 13 1 4
3 4 1 2 14 1 4
3 1 2 14 1 4
2 15 1 4
2 15 1 4
1 5 10 1 2
1 4 7 1 1
9 7
12 1
10 2
9 3
2 1 8
6 1 8
9 12
10 1 1
8 12
2 2 1 1 1 3
1 2 1 2
2 1 2
1 1 1 2 2
1 1 1 1 2
1 1 3 4
1 1 3 4 2
3 13 5
2 1 4 8 8
2 9 1 4 10
2 1 7 1 1 12
2 6 1 2 9 4
2 5 2 2 8 4
11 2 2 9 4
2 4 2 3 9 4
2 4 2 2 11 3
2 3 3 2 11 3
2 6 3 11 1
2 6 2 13
2 5 2 13
2 4 3 13
2 4 2 13
2 3 3 1 8 1
2 6 4 2
2 5 1 9 1
2 5 4 1
2 4 13
2 3 14 1
2 2 13 2
2 14 3

406 DOES IT ALL ADD UP? ★★

The numbers 1-8 have been inserted into the grid so that no two consecutive numbers appear in the same row or column. Any number may appear up to four times. The numbers on the left and above show the totals of the numbers in the row and column respectively. There are no 7s; there is only one 3 which is immediately below a 5; the four centre numbers total 18 and are all different; the numbers in the diagonal top right to bottom left total 14. Can you complete the grid?

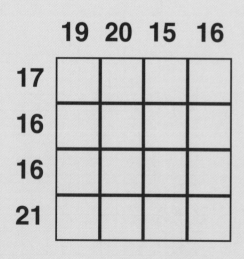

	19	20	15	16
17				
16				
16				
21				

407 DOMINOES ★

Arrange the dominoes so that the spots at both ends of each arrow are the same, as they would be in a normal game.

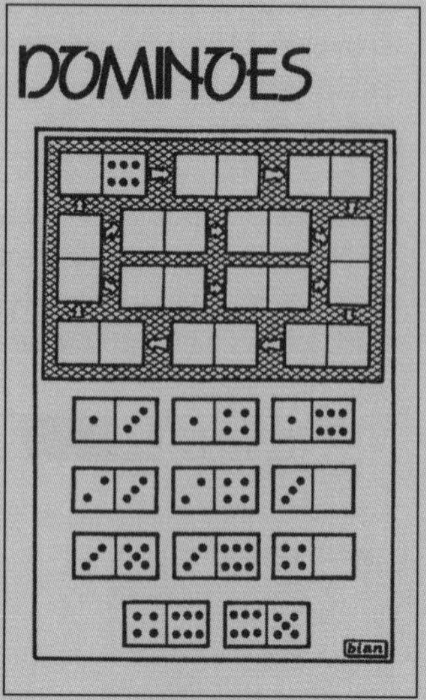
DOMINOES
blan

408   UNLUCKY FOR SOME

Each of the white squares in the diagram contains a different one of the numbers 1 to 13. From the clues given below, can you place the correct number in each of the squares?

Clues

1   There are no two-digit numbers in rows A or D, or in columns 1 or 4.
2   The 9 does not occupy a corner square.
3   The 6 is in direct line below the 2.
4   The number in E5 is one below the one in A3.
5   The 1 is diagonally below and to the left of the 12, and diagonally above and to the right of the 10.
6   The number in square B4 is two higher than the one in square D2.
7   The 8 is in direct line above the number 13.

Starting tip: Start by placing the 1 in its correct position.

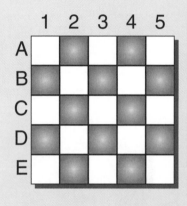

409   TSUNAMI   ★★★

The numbers alongside each row or column tell you how many blocks of black squares are in a line. For example: 2, 3, 5 tells you that from left to right (or top to bottom) there is a group of two black squares, then at least one white space, then a group of three black squares, then at least one white shape, then a group of five black squares. Each block of black squares on the same line must have at least one white square between it and the next block of black squares.

Sometimes it is possible to tell which squares are going to be black without reference to other lines or columns. In the example below, we can deduce that any block of six black squares must incorporate the two central squares:

6 

Can you complete this tsunami puzzle, to reveal the hidden pattern or picture?

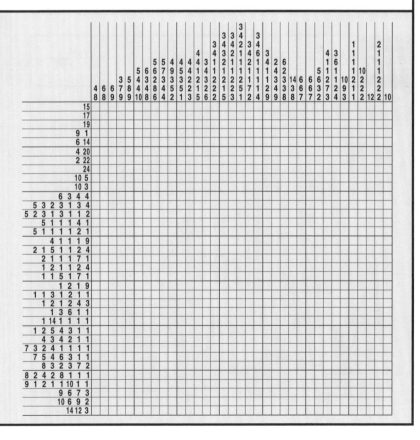

410   LOST IN TRANSIT

Karen moves to a new flat, but almost regrets it when she discovers that the removal men have mislaid some of her possessions – six, to be exact – and have damaged one other. Which are missing, and which has been damaged?

411   TWIN SET

These twins always like to have everything the same as each other, and are looking for two identical lamps. Can you spot them?

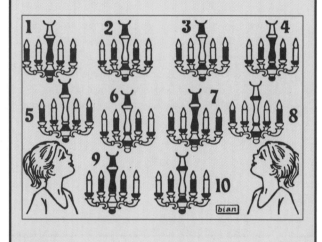

412   ARTISTIC LICENCE ★

Our illustrator has made ten errors in this scene – some of them obvious, others not so easy to spot. Can you identify them all?

413   COG-ITATE

When the handle is turned in the direction shown, which two of the four weights will rise and which two will fall?

414 NOT WELCOME! ★

Can you find the detail missing from each picture which is present in the other three?

416 TOY TANGLE ★

John, Joe and Sue are having fun! Can you work out which prize each child is going to win?

415 TSUNAMI ★★

The numbers alongside each row or column tell you how many blocks of black squares are in a line. For example: 2, 3, 5 tells you that from left to right (or top to bottom) there is a group of two black squares, then at least one white space, then a group of three black squares, then at least one white shape, then a group of five black squares. Each block of black squares on the same line must have at least one white square between it and the next block of black squares.

Sometimes it is possible to tell which squares are going to be black without reference to other lines or columns. In the example below, we can deduce that any block of six black squares must incorporate the two central squares:

6 [ ][ ][ ][ ][■][■][ ][ ][ ][ ]

Can you complete this tsunami puzzle, to reveal the hidden pattern or picture?

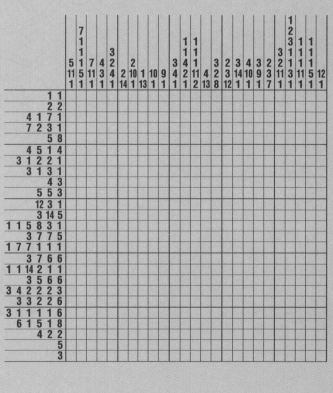

417 TANGLED TAPE ★

Telly-mad Trevor sent four videos to the Fallaboutlaughing show. One was accepted. Follow the tangled tape from the film. The correct film will finish at Trev's camcorder.

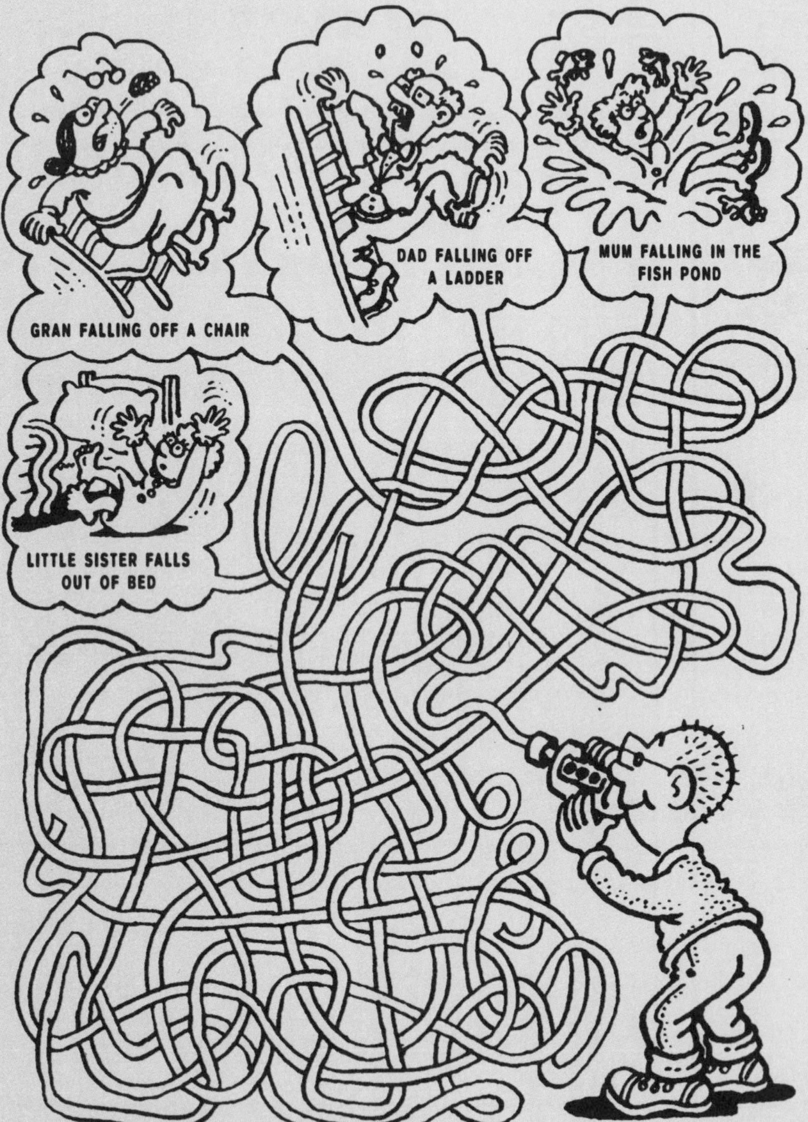

GRAN FALLING OFF A CHAIR

DAD FALLING OFF A LADDER

MUM FALLING IN THE FISH POND

LITTLE SISTER FALLS OUT OF BED

418 TSUNAMI ★★

The numbers alongside each row or column tell you how many blocks of black squares are in a line. For example: 2, 3, 5 tells you that from left to right (or top to bottom) there is a group of two black squares, then at least one white space, then a group of three black squares, then at least one white shape, then a group of five black squares. Each block of black squares on the same line must have at least one white square between it and the next block of black squares.

Sometimes it is possible to tell which squares are going to be black without reference to other lines or columns. In the example below, we can deduce that any block of six black squares must incorporate the two central squares:

6

Can you complete this tsunami puzzle, to reveal the hidden pattern or picture?

419   ON THE SCENE   ★

Each of the six objects in the lower boxes can be found in one of the lettered squares in the big picture. Find these squares and transfer the letters to the little boxes below. You should spell out the name of an English city.

420   TSUNAMI   ★★★

The numbers alongside each row or column tell you how many blocks of black squares are in a line. For example: 2, 3, 5 tells you that from left to right (or top to bottom) there is a group of two black squares, then at least one white space, then a group of three black squares, then at least one white shape, then a group of five black squares. Each block of black squares on the same line must have at least one white square between it and the next block of black squares.

Sometimes it is possible to tell which squares are going to be black without reference to other lines or columns. In the example below, we can deduce that any block of six black squares must incorporate the two central squares:

6 ▢▢▢▢■▢▢▢▢

Can you complete this tsunami puzzle, to reveal the hidden pattern or picture?

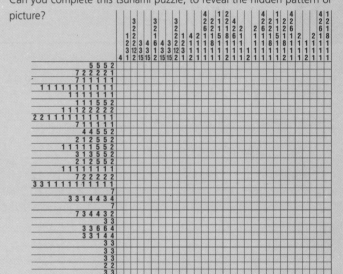

421   SQUARE LETTERS   ★★

The letters of the alphabet, excluding Z, are entered randomly into a 5 x 5 square so that no two consecutive letters are in the same row or column, or in a diagonal in any direction. The letters NQG can be read downwards as can TMO. Square E5 is a vowel. D is immediately left of V and immediately above I, which is not in column 2. Row D begins and ends with a vowel, the first alphabetically preceding the latter. Q and T are at opposite ends of a row, and K and S are at the top and bottom respectively of a column. U is diagonally immediately below W; E and R can both be seen on the same long diagonal. C is diagonally adjacent to H; Y is to the immediate right of F, and X is in a corner square.

Can you locate each letter?

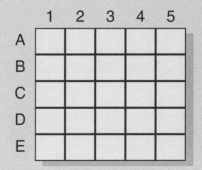

422   LOGI-PATH   ★★

Use your deductive reasoning to form a pathway from the box marked START to the box marked FINISH moving in either direction horizontally or vertically (but not diagonally). The number at the beginning of every row or column indicates exactly how many boxes in that row or column your pathway must pass through. The small diagram is given as an example of how it works.

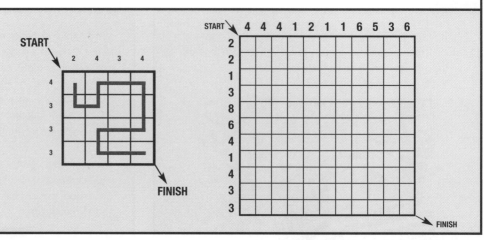

423   LOGISTICAL   ★★★

I bought a parrot recently, intending to teach him to talk. Unfortunately, it seemed that someone had got there before me. I had five visitors on different days last week – two relatives and three men who came to repair things – and the parrot responded to their courteous greetings extremely rudely. From the clues given below, can you work out when each visitor called and how he or she greeted my parrot, and can you also decide what rude response the parrot came out with in each case?

Clues

1 The man who came to the house on Wednesday greeted the parrot with a chirpy "Good morning"; the gasman's visit took place the following day.

2 "Get out of here!" was the bird's response to the person who said, "Nice to meet you".

3 The TV repairman was not the person the parrot told to "Buzz off!".

4 The plumber greeted my pet by saying "Hello"; he was not my Tuesday visitor, who was told by the parrot to "Get lost!"

5 My sister, who did not visit on Monday, spoke her greeting with a friendly smile, and was taken aback when the bird responded with a curt "Go away!".

6 Friday's visitor was not the person whose words to the parrot were, "Who's a pretty boy?"

	Aunt	Gasman	Plumber	TV repairman	Sister	'Good morning'	'Hello'	'How do you do?'	'Nice to meet you'	'Who's a pretty boy?'	'Beat it!'	'Buzz off!'	'Get lost!'	'Get out of here!'	'Go away!'
Monday															
Tuesday															
Wednesday															
Thursday															
Friday															
'Beat it!'															
'Buzz off!'															
'Get lost!'															
'Get out of here!'															
'Go away!'															
'Good morning'															
'Hello'															
'How do you do?'															
'Nice to meet you'															
'Who's a pretty boy?'															

Record in this grid all the information obtained from the clues, by using a cross to indicate a definite 'no' and a tick to show a definite 'yes'. Transfer these to all sections of the grid thus eliminating all but one possibility, which must be the correct one.

Day	Visitor	Greeting	Response

424   SUM-UP   ★

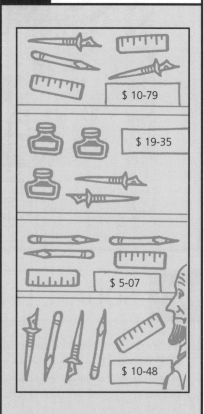

Calculate the price of each pen, pencil, ruler and bottle of ink.

425 NUMBER JIG

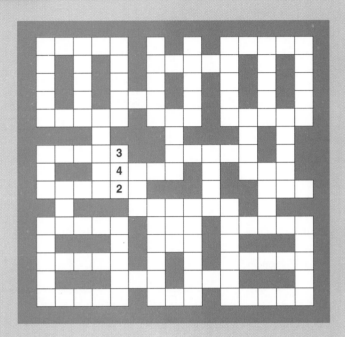

Fit the numbers into the grid as quickly as possible.
One has been done for you.

3 figures	4 figures	41892	81655
237	1358	43914	83199
(342)	2369	50326	89093
402	3743	50371	93721
418	5606	51169	99206
451		52049	
513	5 figures	54102	6 figures
625	14268	59322	138261
686	16999	61505	283863
705	20294	62008	659144
748	23776	62259	764132
814	25358	71703	841023
950	35010	75882	
974	39092	81556	
988	41636		

426 TSUNAMI

The numbers alongside each row or column tell you how many blocks of black squares are in a line. For example: 2, 3, 5 tells you that from left to right (or top to bottom) there is a group of two black squares, then at least one white space, then a group of three black squares, then at least one white shape, then a group of five black squares. Each block of black squares on the same line must have at least one white square between it and the next block of black squares.

Sometimes it is possible to tell which squares are going to be black without reference to other lines or columns. In the example below, we can deduce that any block of six black squares must incorporate the two central squares:

6 ▢▢▢▢▢■■▢▢▢▢

Can you complete this tsunami puzzle, to reveal the hidden pattern or picture?

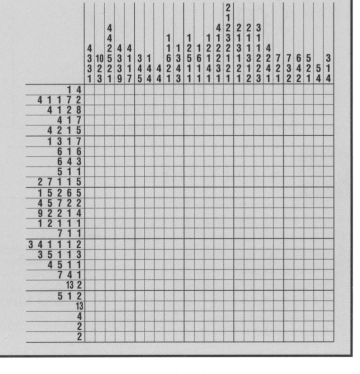

427   WHO'S WHO?   ★

Can you match each doctor to his patient?

428   TSUNAMI   ★★

The numbers alongside each row or column tell you how many blocks of black squares are in a line. For example: 2, 3, 5 tells you that from left to right (or top to bottom) there is a group of two black squares, then at least one white space, then a group of three black squares, then at least one white shape, then a group of five black squares. Each block of black squares on the same line must have at least one white square between it and the next block of black squares.

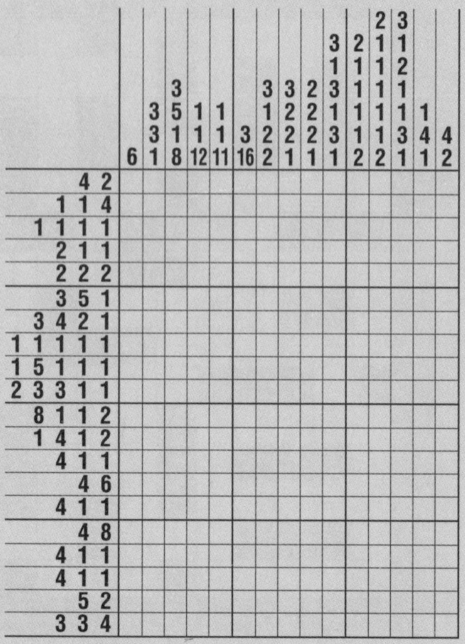

Row clues (top to bottom):
4 2
1 1 4
1 1 1 1
2 1 1
2 2 2
3 5 1
3 4 2 1
1 1 1 1 1
1 5 1 1 1
2 3 3 1 1
8 1 1 2
1 4 1 2
4 1 1
4 6
4 1 1
4 8
4 1 1
4 1 1
5 2
3 3 4

Column clues:
6 1 | 3 3 | 3 5 1 | 1 8 | 1 | 1 | 3 | 3 1 2 | 2 2 2 | 2 2 2 | 3 1 3 1 | 3 1 1 1 1 | 2 1 1 2 1 | 1 2 1 1 2 | 2 3 1 2 2 | 1 1 3 1 | 4 4 1 | 4 2

Sometimes it is possible to tell which squares are going to be black without reference to other lines or columns. In the example below, we can deduce that any block of six black squares must incorporate the two central squares:

6 ▢▢▢▢■▢▢▢▢

Can you complete this tsunami puzzle, to reveal the hidden pattern or picture?

429   FAMILY TREE   ★★

Using the family tree, can you solve the following questions?
1 What is Sally and Andrew's unmarried daughter called?
2 What relation is Victor to Beth?
3 Which couple has the most children?
4 What relation is Billy to Simon?
5 Who in the family is Andy named after?
6 How many grandchildren have Sally and Andrew?
7 Which couple has two children?

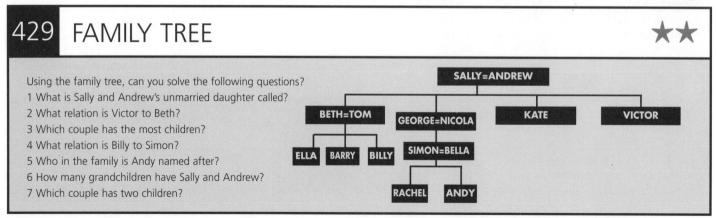

430 DROP OUT

The professor is choosing a book. In the bottom picture, he has made his choice. Which one has he bought?

431 STAG NIGHT ★★★

It was the eve of Tom Toper's wedding, and his pals were determined to make his last night of freedom a memorable one. They celebrated in each of the five pubs in the village – can you discover the order in which they were visited, the name of the landlord or landlady of each pub and the location of each pub?

Clues

A The evening started at the Golden Goose and finished in Gasworks Lane.

B The Green Dragon was not the next port of call after the Black Bull in Mill Street.

C Toby Jugge served the party earlier than Ivor Goodale in Factory Road, but later than Jean-Ann Tonic at the Red Lion.

D Ava Nother could consider herself fortunate that the party visited her establishment before the pub in Waterworks Alley.

	Black Bull	Golden Goose	Green Dragon	Red Lion	White Horse	Ava Nother	Ivor Goodale	Jean-Ann Tonic	Phil Emupp	Toby Jugge	Factory Road	Gasworks Lane	Mill Street	Railway Approach	Waterworks Alley
First															
Second															
Third															
Fourth															
Fifth															
Factory Road															
Gasworks Lane															
Mill Street															
Railway Approach															
Waterworks Alley															
Ava Nother															
Ivor Goodale															
Jean-Ann Tonic															
Phil Emupp															
Toby Jugge															

Record in this grid all the information obtained from the clues, by using a cross to indicate a definite 'no' and a tick to show a definite 'yes'. Transfer these to all sections of the grid thus eliminating all but one possibility, which must be the correct one.

Order	Name of pub	Landlord/lady	Location

432 RED, WHITE AND BLUE ★★

Each cell of the square is coloured red, white or blue. Each row, each column and each of the two long diagonals contains exactly two cells of each colour. The information in each clue refers only to the cells in that row or column. From the clues below, can you tell which colour each cell is?

1 The reds are between the blues.
2 The whites are adjacent.
3 The whites are between the reds.
4 The blues are to the right of the reds.

5 No two squares of the same colour are adjacent.
6 The blues are between the whites.

A The blues are adjacent.
B Each white is immediately above a blue.
C No two squares of the same colour are adjacent.
D The whites are above the reds.
E The whites are above the blues.
F The reds are above the whites.

	A	B	C	D	E	F
1						
2						
3						
4						
5						
6						

433 HALF AND HALF ★

Here are nine mixed-up pots: can you match up the black left halves with their white counterparts?

434 TSUNAMI ★★

The numbers alongside each row or column tell you how many blocks of black squares are in a line. For example: 2, 3, 5 tells you that from left to right (or top to bottom) there is a group of two black squares, then at least one white space, then a group of three black squares, then at least one white shape, then a group of five black squares. Each block of black squares on the same line must have at least one white square between it and the next block of black squares.

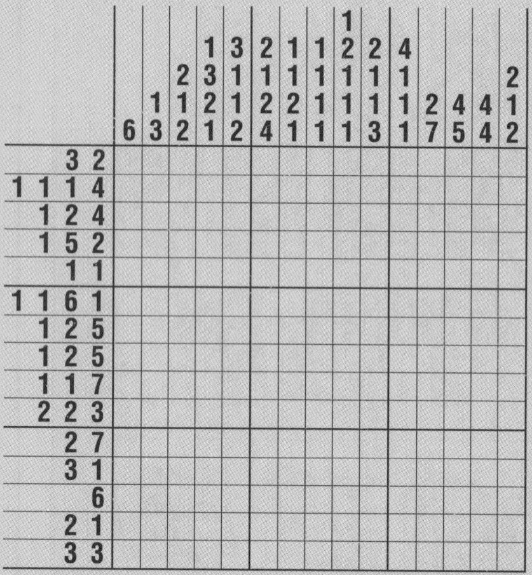

Sometimes it is possible to tell which squares are going to be black without reference to other lines or columns. In the example below, we can deduce that any block of six black squares must incorporate the two central squares:

6

Can you complete this tsunami puzzle, to reveal the hidden pattern or picture?

Column clues (top):

									1			4						
		1	3	2	1	1	2	2		4		1						
	1	3	1	1	2	1	1	1	1	1		1					2	
	1	2	1	2	2	4	1	1	1	1	3	1	2	4	4	2
6	3	2	1	2	4	1	1	1	1	3	1	1	7	5	4	2

Row clues (left):

Row	Clue
1	3 2
2	1 1 1 4
3	1 2 4
4	1 5 2
5	1 1
6	1 1 6 1
7	1 2 5
8	1 2 5
9	1 1 7
10	2 2 3
11	2 7
12	3 1
13	6
14	2 1
15	3 3

435 FITBITS ★

The Groggins Gang celebrates another successful raid – but can you be successful in discovering which two of the five details shown below (which might be displayed at a different angle from the original) belong to which two villains?

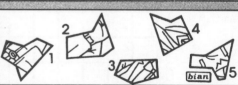

436 TWISTING TRAILS ★

Messy Mandy has mixed up her favourite toys! Follow the lines to sort them out.

437 FIGUREWORK ★★

Fit the numbers into the grid as quickly as possible. We have done one for you.

2 figures	4 figures	7 figures
26	2049	2148471
47	3251	5739600
60	4788	
93	5177	**9 figures**
	6074	285092204
3 figures	7756	330518140
229	(8352)	
307	9703	
480		
549	**5 figures**	
738	39214	
816	68644	

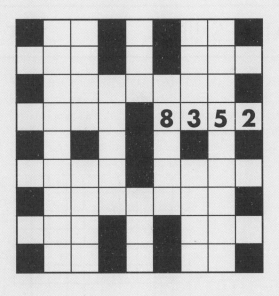

438 ROYALIST REVELS ★

The Cavaliers have fought their battles and are relaxing after a famous victory. Two of them have a special reason for celebration – they were the only comrades to share the same battles, as their identical medals bear witness. Who are they?

439 TWISTING TRAILS ★

Help Farmer Barley reach his sheep and then find his way with his flock to the sheep pen.

440 TSUNAMI

The numbers alongside each row or column tell you how many blocks of black squares are in a line. For example: 2, 3, 5 tells you that from left to right (or top to bottom) there is a group of two black squares, then at least one white space, then a group of three black squares, then at least one white shape, then a group of five black squares. Each block of black squares on the same line must have at least one white square between it and the next block of black squares. Sometimes it is possible to tell which squares are going to be black without reference to other lines or columns. In the example below, we can deduce that any block of six black squares must incorporate the two central squares:

6

Can you complete this tsunami puzzle, to reveal the hidden pattern or picture?

Row clues (top to bottom):
- 12
- 2 2 3
- 1 3 1 3
- 1 2 1 2 1
- 1 1 1 2 1
- 18
- 1 3
- 18 1
- 11 1 1 2 1
- 1 3 2 1 1 1 1
- 3 1 3 8
- 2 2 2 2 1 3
- 1 1 1 1 1 1 2 2 2
- 2 2 2 9 1
- 3 3 2 2

---

441 SILHOUETTE ★

Shade in every fragment containing a dot – and what have you got?

---

442 BATTLESHIPS ★★

Do you remember the old game of battleships? This puzzle is based on that idea. Your task is to find the vessels in the diagram. Some parts of boats or sea squares have already been filled in, and a number next to a row or column refers to the number of occupied squares in that row or column. The boats may be positioned horizontally or vertically, but no two boats or parts of boats are in adjacent squares – horizontally, vertically or diagonally.

Aircraft carrier: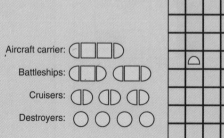
Battleships:
Cruisers:
Destroyers:

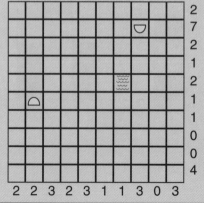

443 ROUTINE WORK

Amy Witherspoon is a methodical soul who believes that routine equals efficiency. When she retired recently after working for 45 years in a department store, she organised her week so that she has one principal activity every morning, afternoon and evening. From the following information, can you work out Amy's Monday to Friday timetable?

Clues

A Monday is the day for mopping the kitchen floor, but not for choir practice; Amy does her weekly shop on Tuesday.

B Washing-day is immediately followed by ironing-day, which is not on the same day as going to either the library or the art class, both of which activities occur on different days.

C Amy does her baking on the morning of her friend's visit, so that they can have fresh cakes for tea, and so that Amy can take some to her sister, whom she visits the next afternoon.

D The weekly whist drive takes place the day after bingo and the day before Amy does her ironing; she likes to have her hair done on Friday, so that she looks her best for the weekend.

Record in this grid all the information obtained from the clues, by using a cross to indicate a definite 'no' and a tick to show a definite 'yes'. Transfer these to all sections of the grid thus eliminating all but one possibility, which must be the correct one.

Day	Morning	Afternoon	Evening

444 FISHY TALE ★

Hugh took a photo of his son standing in front of the aquarium at the zoo. Which fish in the tank is the same as the one in the photo?

445 HANG IT ★

To the left are four abstract paintings. To the right Jim is trying to work out which one he's bought and which way up it's supposed to be. Can you help him?

446 KNOT SO ★

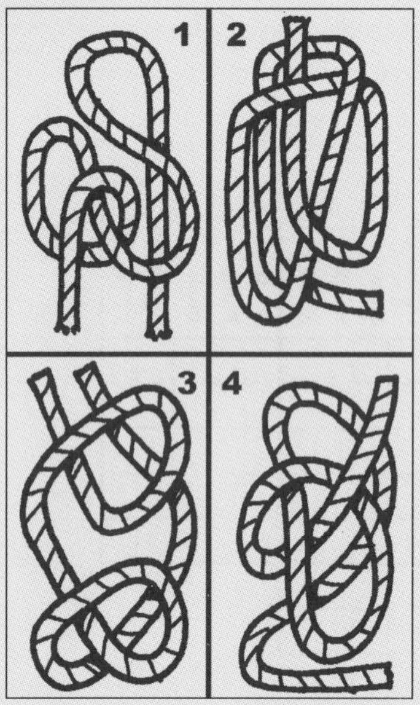
1
2
3
4

Which tangles will knot when pulled and which will not?

447 TSUNAMI ★★

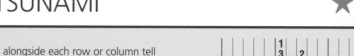

The numbers alongside each row or column tell you how many blocks of black squares are in a line. For example: 2, 3, 5 tells you that from left to right (or top to bottom) there is a group of two black squares, then at least one white space, then a group of three black squares, then at least one white shape, then a group of five black squares. Each block of black squares on the same line must have at least one white square between it and the next block of black squares.

Sometimes it is possible to tell which squares are going to be black without reference to other lines or columns. In the example below, we can deduce that any block of six black squares must incorporate the two central squares:

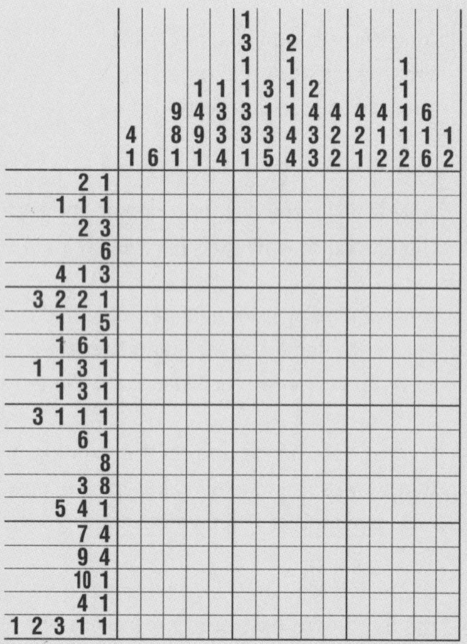
4 1
6
9 8 1
1 4 9 1
1 3 3 4
1 3 1 1 3 3 1
3 1 3 5
2 1 1 1 4 4
2 4 3 3
4 2 2
4 2 1
4 1 2
1 1 1 1 2
6 1 6
1 2
2 1
1 1 1
2 3
6
4 1 3
3 2 2 1
1 1 5
1 6 1
1 1 3 1
1 3 1
3 1 1 1
6 1
8
3 8
5 4 1
7 4
9 4
10 1
4 1
1 2 3 1 1

6 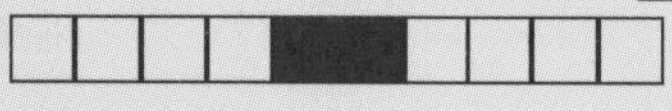

Can you complete this tsunami puzzle, to reveal the hidden pattern or picture?

448 PEEL ME A GRAPE ★

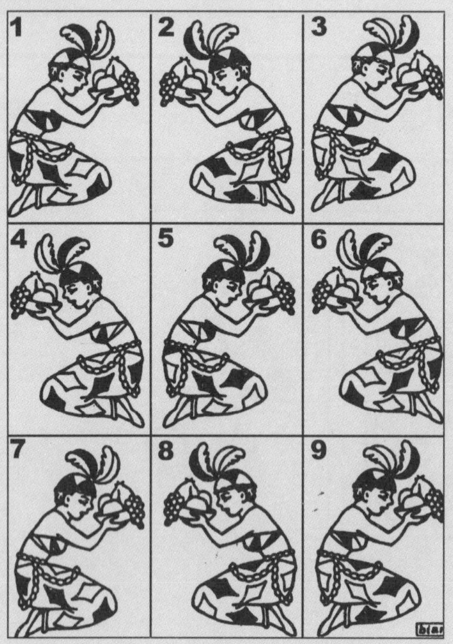
1
2
3
4
5
6
7
8
9

Four of the serving-girls have mirror-images. Which are the four pairs, and which is the odd-girl-out?

449 WHAT'S THE POINT? ★★

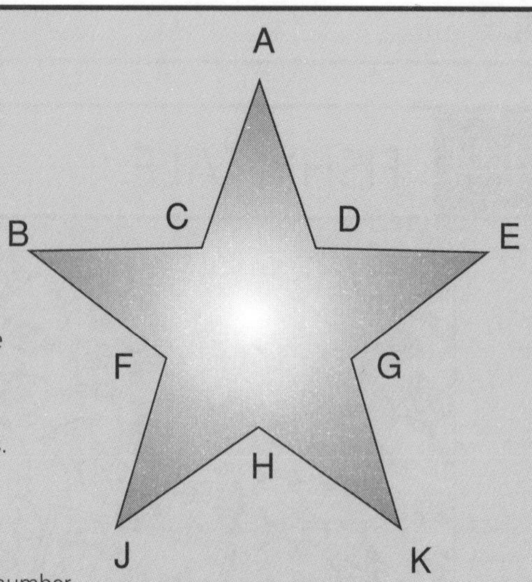
A
B
C
D
E
F
G
H
J
K

Each number from 1 to 10 appears once in this star, either at a point or at an intersection. The numbers 2, 10, 5 and 3 appear in that order along one line. 1 is on the central pentagon and 9 is at one of the star's five points. 8 and 6 are at opposite ends of one of the lines, while 4 is the next number clockwise from 7 in the pentagon. The numbers at A and D total 10, as do those at G and K. 10 is located higher than 1 but lower than 8. Where is each number?

450 | TSUNAMI ★★

The numbers alongside each row or column tell you how many blocks of black squares are in a line. For example: 2, 3, 5 tells you that from left to right (or top to bottom) there is a group of two black squares, then at least one white space, then a group of three black squares, then at least one white shape, then a group of five black squares. Each block of black squares on the same line must have at least one white square between it and the next block of black squares.

Sometimes it is possible to tell which squares are going to be black without reference to other lines or columns. In the example below, we can deduce that any block of six black squares must incorporate the two central squares:

6 ☐☐☐☐■☐☐☐☐

Can you complete this tsunami puzzle, to reveal the hidden pattern or picture?

Row clues (top to bottom):
- 9 1
- 4 1 2
- 1 1 1 2 1 1
- 1 1 1 2
- 1 1 1 1 2
- 1 4 1 2
- 1 6 1 2
- 1 11 2
- 2 6 4
- 3 2 11
- 4 2 2 6
- 6 4 1 6
- 6 2 3 5
- 8 1 2 4
- 7 1 6 4
- 6 1 1 10
- 7 3 4
- 5 3 1 5
- 4 1 8
- 6 2 9
- 4 4 10
- 2 9
- 2 8
- 2 5 2
- 3 4 5

451 | BOX CLEVER ★

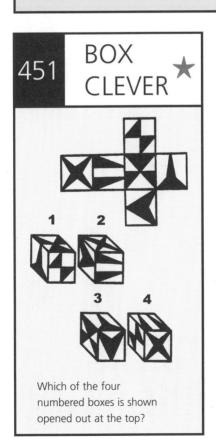

Which of the four numbered boxes is shown opened out at the top?

452 | SILHOUETTE ★

Shade all of the shapes containing a dot to reveal a picture.

453 | HAT TRICK ★

Acchooo! All these feathers are making me sneeze. How quickly can you put the pictures in order, from the smallest feather to the largest feather?

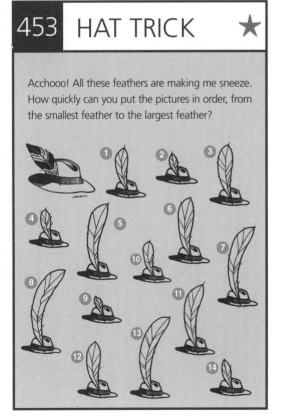

454 TSUNAMI ★★

The numbers alongside each row or column tell you how many blocks of black squares are in a line. For example: 2, 3, 5 tells you that from left to right (or top to bottom) there is a group of two black squares, then at least one white space, then a group of three black squares, then at least one white shape, then a group of five black squares. Each block of black squares on the same line must have at least one white square between it and the next block of black squares.

Sometimes it is possible to tell which squares are going to be black without reference to other lines or columns. In the example below, we can deduce that any block of six black squares must incorporate the two central squares:

6 ☐☐☐☐■■☐☐☐☐

Can you complete this tsunami puzzle, to reveal the hidden pattern or picture?

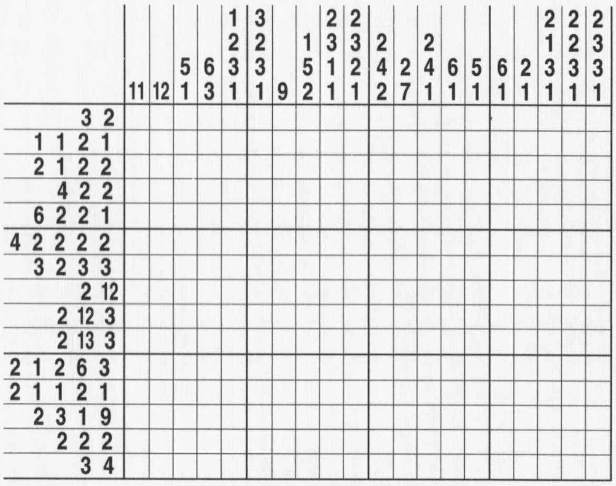
Columns: 11 | 12 | 5 1 | 6 3 | 1 2 3 1 | 3 2 3 1 | 9 | 1 5 2 | 2 3 1 1 | 2 3 2 1 | 2 4 2 | 2 7 | 2 4 1 | 6 1 | 5 1 | 6 1 | 2 1 | 2 1 3 1 | 2 2 3 1 | 2 3 3 1
Rows: 3 2 | 1 1 2 1 | 2 1 2 2 | 4 2 2 | 6 2 2 1 | 4 2 2 2 2 | 3 2 3 3 | 2 12 | 2 12 3 | 2 13 3 | 2 1 2 6 3 | 2 1 1 2 1 | 2 3 1 9 | 2 2 2 | 3 4

455 BATTLESHIPS ★★

Do you remember the old game of battleships? This puzzle is based on that idea. Your task zis to find the vessels in the diagram. Some parts of boats or sea squares have already been filled in, and a number next to a row or column refers to the number of occupied squares in that row or column. The boats may be positioned horizontally or vertically, but no two boats or parts of boats are in adjacent squares – horizontally, vertically or diagonally.

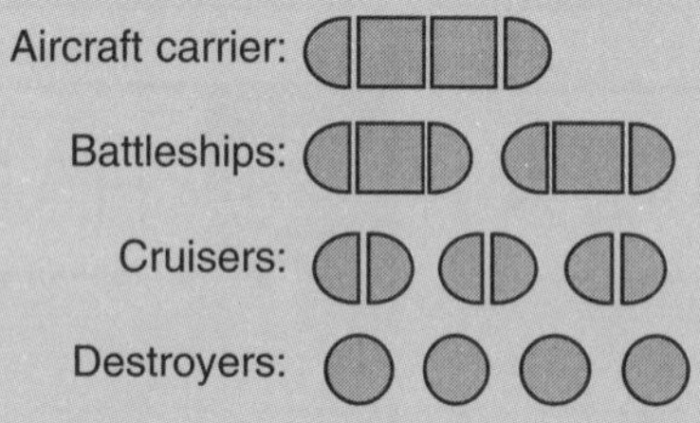
Aircraft carrier:
Battleships:
Cruisers:
Destroyers:

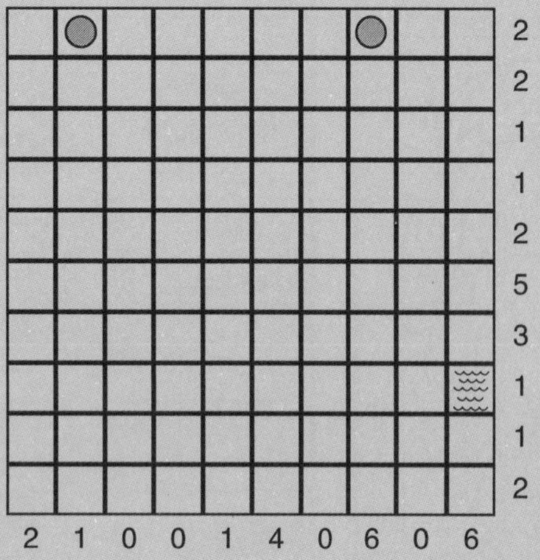
2
2
1
1
2
5
3
1
1
2
2 1 0 0 1 4 0 6 0 6

456 ROCKY'S JOIN THE DOTS ★

Join the dots to find out why the cave boy and the dinosaur are hiding underneath this rock.

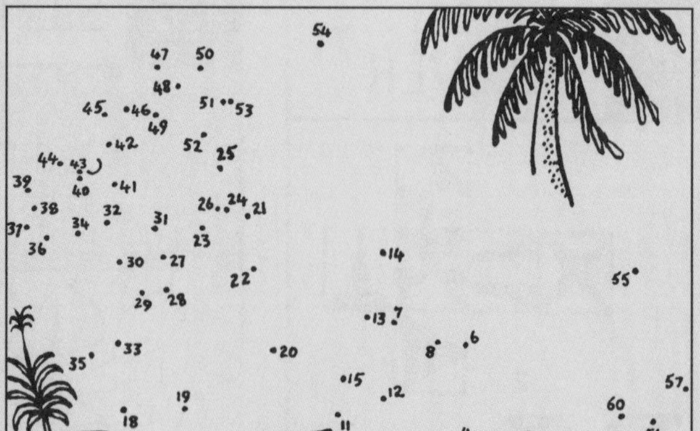

457 LOGISTICAL

Since buying a metal-detector, Derek has been taking every opportunity to search for buried valuables. Last week, he took his new toy out on five occasions, but took so long to find anything at all each time that he gave up in despair when the first item he dug up proved to be little better than rubbish. From the clues given below, can you put Derek's five excursions into their correct order, saying where he went, how long he spent searching and what he eventually found on each occasion?

Clues

1 The rusty doorknob turned up after a 20-minute search, but not in Derek's garden.

2 On the third occasion he used his metal-detector, Derek spent over half an hour searching in a farmer's field, but it was not that day that he went home having found only a bottle top.

3 The trip to the park yielded nothing but an old spoon.

4 Derek's fourth attempt at locating hidden riches culminated in the discovery of a spanner after a search lasting for less than 40 minutes; the 25-minute hunt on a beach had taken place before this.

5 The treasure-hunter's second outing with his metal-detector lasted for just 15 minutes.

Order	Place	Time spent	Item found

Record in this grid all the information obtained from the clues, by using a cross to indicate a definite 'no' and a tick to show a definite 'yes'. Transfer these to all sections of the grid thus eliminating all but one possibility, which must be the correct one.

458 IT'S TRICKY ★

These rabbits are stumped! The numbers next to the grid show what symbols those rows or columns add up to. See if you can work out what number each symbol stands for, and what number should replace the question mark beneath the first column.

459 CHINESE I-SPY

There are six pairs of identical squares in this picture of the Great Wall of China. Can you spot them?

460 MINIMAZE

Each obstacle along the maze's path carries a penalty (as shown in the central box). See if you can find your way from A to B, while incurring a total of 40 penalty points.

461 PICTURE PUZZLER

Shade all the shapes that have a dot in, to find out what's going on here.

462 TSUNAMI

The numbers alongside each row or column tell you how many blocks of black squares are in a line. For example: 2, 3, 5 tells you that from left to right (or top to bottom) there is a group of two black squares, then at least one white space, then a group of three black squares, then at least one white shape, then a group of five black squares. Each block of black squares on the same line must have at least one white square between it and the next block of black squares.

Sometimes it is possible to tell which squares are going to be black without reference to other lines or columns. In the example below, we can deduce that any block of six black squares must incorporate the two central squares:

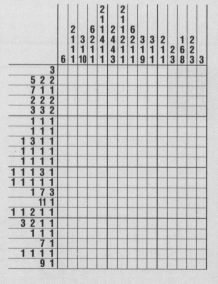

Can you complete this tsunami puzzle, to reveal the hidden pattern or picture?

463 LOGISTICAL ★★★

Canine psychiatrist Jack Russell has been consulted by the owners of five animals with behavioural problems. From the clues below, can you work out the name and breed of each person's pet, and say what its problem is?

Clues

1 Miss Flatman's dog, Eddie, is not the whippet with a morbid fear of cats.

2 The animal with what the owner describes as 'anti-social habits' has a name beginning with a consonant.

3 Owing to the misplaced generosity of the customers at the pub run by his owner, Flash has become an alcoholic.

4 Ms Scanlon's dog chases policemen, although ignoring other persons in uniform.

5 Mrs Carrick's pet, which isn't the boxer, is sociable and has no fear of other animals.

6 King is a Dalmatian, but Outlaw is not Mr McCrae's corgi.

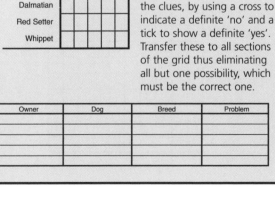

	Eddie	Flash	King	Outlaw	Tiffany	Boxer	Corgi	Dalmatian	Red Setter	Whippet	Alcoholic	Anti-social habits	Chases policemen	Eats flowers	Scared of cats
Mr Baker															
Mrs Carrick															
Miss Flatman															
Mr McCrae															
Ms Scanlon															
Alcoholic															
Anti-social habits															
Chases policemen															
Eats flowers															
Scared of cats															
Boxer															
Corgi															
Dalmatian															
Red Setter															
Whippet															

Record in this grid all the information obtained from the clues, by using a cross to indicate a definite 'no' and a tick to show a definite 'yes'. Transfer these to all sections of the grid thus eliminating all but one possibility, which must be the correct one.

Owner	Dog	Breed	Problem

464 PAINT BOX ★

Arthur has started a painting, but he has got his paint-brushes muddled up. How many paint-brushes can you spot on this page?

465 LATIN SQUARE ★★

The grid is to be filled in with numbers from 1 to 6 so that each number appears exactly once in each row and each column. The clues refer to the digit totals in the squares mentioned. For example, DEF2=9 would mean that the numbers in D2, E2 and F2 add up to 9.

	A	B	C	D	E	F
1						
2						
3						
4						
5						
6						

A456=10 CDE6=14
AB2=5 D345=7
B123=14 E12=7
C123=7 EF4=10
CDE3=6 F123=8

467 IDENTICAL TWINS ★

Which of these two pictures are identical?

466 TV TREV'S BARE OUTLINES ★

When Trev watches TV he gets carried away! He's watching a programme about the Arctic, so he has to dress up in warm clothes. How many polar bears can you count?

468 LOGI-PATH ★★

Use your deductive reasoning to form a pathway from the box marked START to the box marked FINISH moving in either direction horizontally or vertically (but not diagonally). The number at the beginning of every row or column indicates exactly how many boxes in that row or column your pathway must pass through. The small diagram is given as an example of how it works.

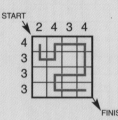

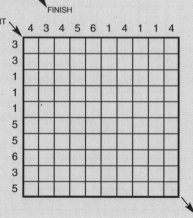

469 VILLAGE TREASURES   ★★★

On each of the approach roads to our village stands a listed building which no longer serves its original purpose, but has been converted into a domestic residence. From the clues given below, can you describe the purpose for which each of the buildings numbered 1 to 4 was first designed, say in which year it was built, and name its present owners?

Clues

1 The railway station, a victim of the infamous Dr Beeching, is the most recent building, having been erected in 1854; it is on the road 90 degrees clockwise from the one on which the property where the Mortons live stands.

2 The building you pass as you enter the village from the north was built in 1825.

3 You go straight on at the crossroads to get from the building dating from 1772 to the old windmill; neither of these buildings now belongs to the Vickers family.

4 Building 3 is older than the one where the Carters live, but not as old as the one-time tollhouse.

5 The home of the Lewis family, which bears an even number on the plan, dates from the 18th century.

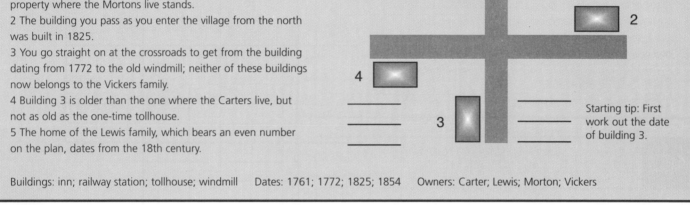

Building: _____
Owner: _____
Date: _____

Starting tip: First work out the date of building 3.

Buildings: inn; railway station; tollhouse; windmill   Dates: 1761; 1772; 1825; 1854   Owners: Carter; Lewis; Morton; Vickers

470 TSUNAMI   ★★★

The numbers alongside each row or column tell you how many blocks of black squares are in a line. For example: 2, 3, 5 tells you that from left to right (or top to bottom) there is a group of two black squares, then at least one white space, then a group of three black squares, then at least one white shape, then a group of five black squares. Each block of black squares on the same line must have at least one white square between it and the next block of black squares.

Sometimes it is possible to tell which squares are going to be black without reference to other lines or columns. In the example below, we can deduce that any block of six black squares must incorporate the two central squares:

6

Can you complete this tsunami puzzle, to reveal the hidden pattern or picture?

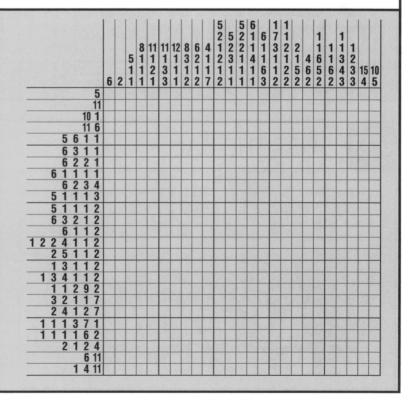

471   LOGISTICAL

There was panic in the court of King Brian when five of the monarch's food-tasters fell ill on consecutive days. At first it was thought that someone was trying to poison the king, but it soon became clear that the cause of the problem was the new chef, whose cooking was so terrible that it was a hazard to human health. From the clues given below, can you work out the order in which the tasters became unwell, and discover which food gave each of them food poisoning and for which meal it was to be served?

Clues

1 Jasper was the taster who was affected immediately before the one who felt distinctly odd after eating some turkey.

2 Eric contracted food poisoning by sampling something intended for the king's lunch one day.

3 The fourth taster to fall ill suffered an unpleasant reaction to some poorly-cooked goose.

4 Chicken was not responsible for laying low the second taster, Alan, who was not the man affected by food prepared for the king's light supper one evening.

5 Oswald, who was not the first taster to become unwell, got food poisoning from some beef, and the very next taster to fall victim to the chef's cooking was poisoned by food due to be served as part of the king's afternoon snack.

6 The last of the five tasters to fall ill did so as a result of eating food intended for a huge evening banquet.

Order	Taster	Food	Meal

Record in this grid all the information obtained from the clues, by using a cross to indicate a definite 'no' and a tick to show a definite 'yes'. Transfer these to all sections of the grid thus eliminating all but one possibility, which must be the correct one.

472   SPOT THE BALL

Sarah has hidden a ball under one of the six upturned teacups. Using the following information, can you say under which of the cups (1 to 6) Sarah has put the ball?

The cup hiding the ball has a cup with a white handle on its immediate left.
The cup hiding the ball has a cup with a rose pattern on its immediate right.
The cup hiding the ball has a different coloured handle from the cup on its immediate left.

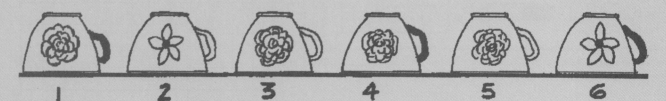

473 BATTLESHIPS ★★

Do you remember the old game of battleships? This puzzle is based on that idea. Your task is to find the vessels in the diagram. Some parts of boats or sea squares have already been filled in, and a number next to a row or column refers to the number of occupied squares in that row or column. The boats may be positioned horizontally or vertically, but no two boats or parts of boats are in adjacent squares – horizontally, vertically or diagonally.

Row totals (top to bottom): 4, 2, 2, 0, 0, 0, 1, 6, 1, 4

Column totals (left to right): 1, 2, 0, 3, 3, 2, 2, 3, 0, 4

Aircraft carrier:
Battleships:
Cruisers:
Destroyers:

474 ARTY ANNIE'S JOIN THE DOTS ★

Trust Annie to make anything but a normal snowman. Join the dots and see her creation.

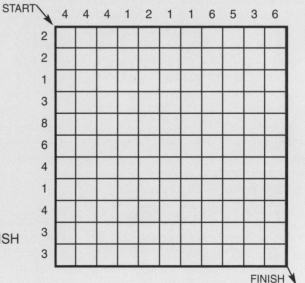

475 LOGI-PATH ★

Use your deductive reasoning to form a pathway from the box marked START to the box marked FINISH moving in either direction horizontally or vertically (but not diagonally). The number at the beginning of every row or column indicates exactly how many boxes in that row or column your pathway must pass through. The small diagram is given as an example of how it works.

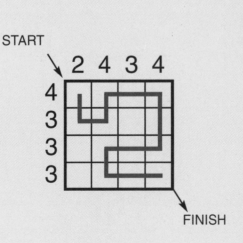

START

	2	4	3	4
4				
3				
3				
3				

FINISH

START →

	4	4	4	1	2	1	1	6	5	3	6
2											
2											
1											
3											
8											
6											
4											
1											
4											
3											
3											

FINISH ↓

476 DOT TO DOT ★

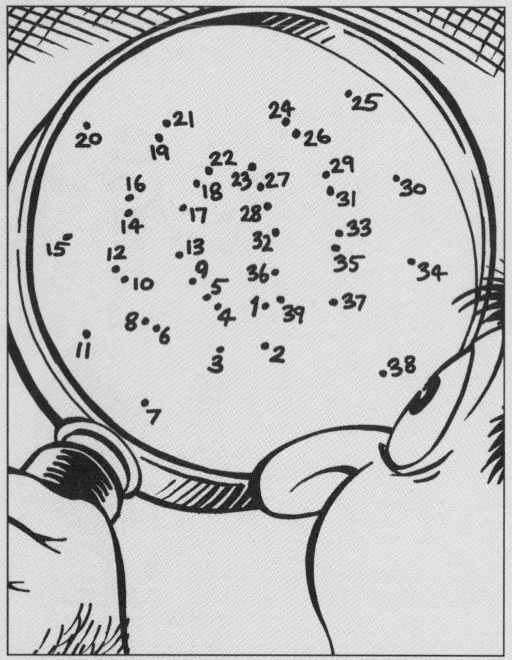

Join the dots to find what's fascinating Stanley!

477 A-MAZING ★

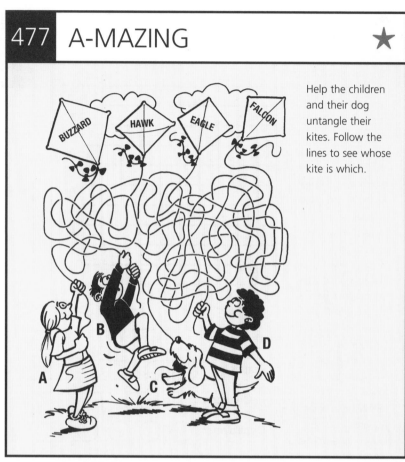

Help the children and their dog untangle their kites. Follow the lines to see whose kite is which.

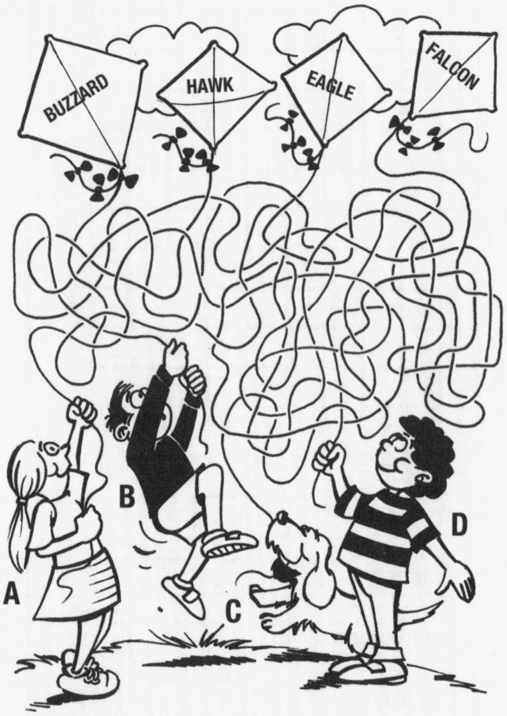
BUZZARD
HAWK
EAGLE
FALCON
A
B
C
D

478 TSUNAMI ★★

The numbers alongside each row or column tell you how many blocks of black squares are in a line. For example: 2, 3, 5 tells you that from left to right (or top to bottom) there is a group of two black squares, then at least one white space, then a group of three black squares, then at least one white shape, then a group of five black squares. Each block of black squares on the same line must have at least one white square between it and the next block of black squares.

Sometimes it is possible to tell which squares are going to be black without reference to other lines or columns. In the example below, we can deduce that any block of six black squares must incorporate the two central squares:

6 

Can you complete this tsunami puzzle, to reveal the hidden pattern or picture?

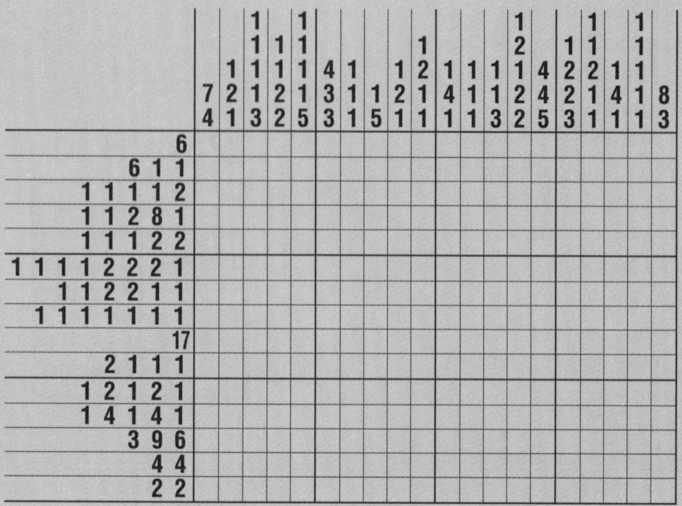
7 4
1 2 1
1 1 1 1 3
1 1 2 2
1 1 1 1 5
4 3 3
1 1 1
1 5
1 2 1
1 2 1 1
1 4 1
1 1 1
1 1 3
1 2 1 2 2
4 4 5
1 2 2 3
1 1 2 1 1
1 4 1
1 1 1 1 1
8 3
6
6 1 1
1 1 1 1 2
1 1 2 8 1
1 1 1 2 2
1 1 1 1 2 2 2 1
1 1 2 2 1 1
1 1 1 1 1 1 1
17
2 1 1 1
1 2 1 2 1
1 4 1 4 1
3 9 6
4 4
2 2

479 PICTURE PUZZLER ★

The shapes below all appear in the picture somewhere, although they may have been rotated or flipped over. Can you spot them?

480 BATTLESHIPS ★★

Do you remember the old game of battleships? This puzzle is based on that idea. Your task is to find the vessels in the diagram. Some parts of boats or sea squares have already been filled in, and a number next to a row or column refers to the number of occupied squares in that row or column. The boats may be positioned horizontally or vertically, but no two boats or parts of boats are in adjacent squares – horizontally, vertically or diagonally.

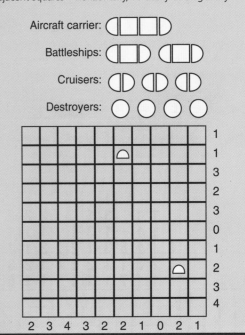

481 STARRY EYED ★

Louise is upset because the stars her teacher stuck in her maths book have become unstuck. How many stars and how many tears can you find hidden in this picture?

482 TWISTING TRAILS ★

Wilfred Worm wants to hurry home without disturbing that hungry-looking bird! Can you help him?

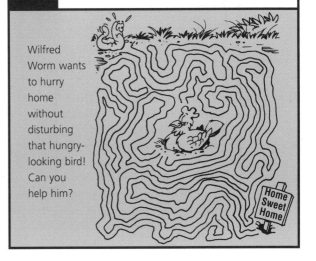

483 TSUNAMI ★★

The numbers alongside each row or column tell you how many blocks of black squares are in a line. For example: 2, 3, 5 tells you that from left to right (or top to bottom) there is a group of two black squares, then at least one white space, then a group of three black squares, then at least one white shape, then a group of five black squares. Each block of black squares on the same line must have at least one white square between it and the next block of black squares.

Sometimes it is possible to tell which squares are going to be black without reference to other lines or columns. In the example below, we can deduce that any block of six black squares must incorporate the two central squares:

6 □□□□■■□□□□

Can you complete this tsunami puzzle, to reveal the hidden pattern or picture?

Column clues (left to right):
6 3 1 | 1 1 1 2 1 | 1 1 1 3 1 | 6 1 7 | 1 3 1 3 1 1 | 1 3 1 2 1 | 1 2 1 1 | 2 4 1 | 2 1 3 1 1 | 2 1 1 2 1 | 2 1 1 3 6 | 1 1 1 10 | 3 4 5 1 | 2 4 1 1 | 1 4 1

Row clues (top to bottom):
6
1 1 1 2
1 1 4 1
1 8 1
1 4 1
6 1
1 1 1
2
8
1 1
6 1 6
1 2 5
7 1 4
5 2 3
3 4
1 2
2 6 2 2
1 2
3 2
6

484 DISCARD ★★★

Remove 35 cards by eliminating each of the seven 'hands' of five cards, leaving one card over.
For each hand, none of the five cards you select must be in the same row or column as any of the others. So which is the discard?

Straight Flush – 5 cards in sequence from the same suit. (Ace follows King.)
Four of a Kind and a Ten.
Run – 5 cards in sequence, any suits.
Flush – any 5 cards of the same suit, not all in sequence.
Full House – three of one kind and two of another kind.
Two Pairs of the same kind and a Seven.
Two Pairs of the same kind and a Ten, total value 38.
(Ace=1, King =13.)

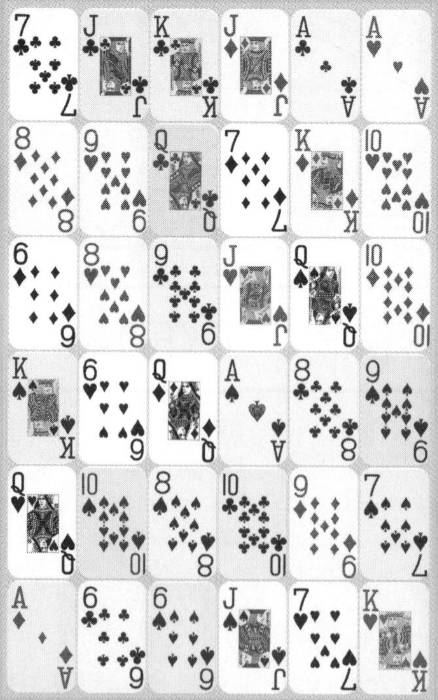

Card Checklist

	6	7	8	9	10	J	Q	K	A
CLUBS									
DIAMONDS									
HEARTS									
SPADES									

485 IDENTICAL TWINS ★

There are two identical butterflies on this page. Which two are they?

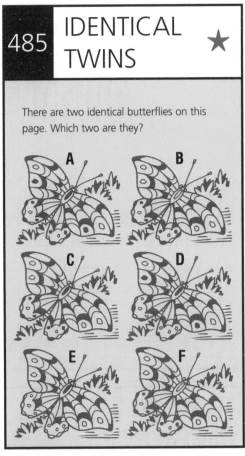

486 NO BIG DEAL ★★★

Four cards were dealt face up on the table by four friends about to draw for partners. By chance, each card dealt was of a different value and a different suit. From the clues given below, can you say who dealt each of cards 1 to 4, and identify each card?

Players: Andrew; Bevis; Charlie; Dean
Values: 2; 5; 8; Jack
Suits: Clubs; Diamonds; Hearts; Spades

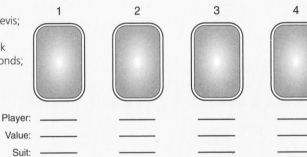

Player: ___ ___ ___ ___
Value: ___ ___ ___ ___
Suit: ___ ___ ___ ___

Starting tip: Begin by working out the value of the Heart.

Clues
1 The card dealt by Bevis was of a higher value than the Heart, which is somewhere to the left of the 8 in the layout.
2 Dean's card was a Diamond.
3 One card was the 5 of Clubs, which is further left on the table than the Spade.
4 Charlie's card was a higher one than card 2.
5 The card dealt by Andrew is two places to the right of the Jack in the deal.

487 ROUNDABOUT ★

Have a careful look at this picture. How many complete circles can you see?

488 SILHOUETTE ★

Shade all the shapes containing a dot to reveal the picture.

489 TSUNAMI ★★

The numbers alongside each row or column tell you how many blocks of black squares are in a line. For example: 2, 3, 5 tells you that from left to right (or top to bottom) there is a group of two black squares, then at least one white space, then a group of three black squares, then at least one white shape, then a group of five black squares. Each block of black squares on the same line must have at least one white square between it and the next block of black squares.

Sometimes it is possible to tell which squares are going to be black without reference to other lines or columns. In the example below, we can deduce that any block of six black squares must incorporate the two central squares:

6 · ☐ ☐ ☐ ☐ ■ ☐ ☐ ☐ ☐ ☐

Can you complete this tsunami puzzle, to reveal the hidden pattern or picture?

```
                          3 2 2 1 1 1
                          2 2 1 1 4 3
                  5 8 4 3 1 1 1 1       3
                  3 4 2 1 1 1 1 1       2
            2 6 9 3 3 2 1 2 2 1 1 6     1 2
          5 6 7 8 4 4 3 2 2 2 2 2 1 1   4 3
      7
    5 1
    4 1
  3 1 1
    7 4
  6 3 1
2 1 1 1 1
3 1 2 1 1
  4 1 3
  5 3 2
    5 1
      6
    3 6
  3 1 2
5 1 1 1
4 2 1 1 1
  5 2 3 1
    6 1
      13
    11 1
```

490 ON THE GREEN ★★★

The diagram shows four players involved in a game of bowls. Each has had one shot, and the player numbered 1 is just about to bowl his second wood. From the clues given below, can you fully identify all four players, and work out what headgear each is wearing (or, in one case, not) to protect him from the hot sun?

Clues

1 As you look at the diagram, Charles is next further down the green from Jacks, who is wearing the straw boater.

2 The bareheaded player, whose surname is not Byass, is in position 3.

3 Walter is not player number 2.

4 James, who is wearing the floppy sunhat, is not number one, the player about to bowl his next wood, whose surname is Green.

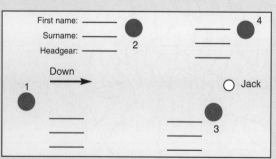

First names: Charles; Donald; James; Walter

Surnames: Byass; Green; Jacks; Wood

Headgear: bareheaded; flat-cap; floppy sunhat; straw boater

Starting tip: Begin by working out what player 1 is wearing on his head.

491 SPOT THE DIFFERENCE ★

Find eight differences between these pictures.

492 | BATTLESHIPS

Do you remember the old game of battleships? This puzzle is based on that idea. Your task is to find the vessels in the diagram. Some parts of boats or sea squares have already been filled in, and a number next to a row or column refers to the number of occupied squares in that row or column. The boats may be positioned horizontally or vertically, but no two boats or parts of boats are in adjacent squares – horizontally, vertically or diagonally.

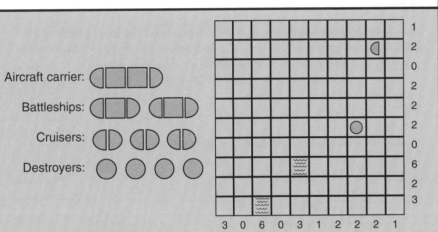

Aircraft carrier:

Battleships:

Cruisers:

Destroyers:

493 | DEER DEER ★

Can you spot 10 differences between the reindeers' Christmas parties?

494 | SPOT THE DIFFERENCE ★

Can you spot eight differences between the two pictures?

495 BRIDGE BREAK ★★★

Four students were playing bridge at a table in the corner of the union building at a college of Goatsferry University. From the clues given below, can you fully identify the player in each of the four seats, and name the subject he or she is reading?

Clues

1 The player in the North seat is studying for a degree in engineering.

2 Karen, the law student, is partnered by Ruff.

3 Amanda Hart is in the seat 90 degrees anticlockwise from the theology student.

4 The medical student, Shuffell, is not Petra.

First names: Amanda; Josephine; Karen; Petra

Surnames: Diamond; Hart; Ruff; Shuffell

Subjects: engineering; law; medicine; theology

Starting tip: Begin by naming the subject studied by Amanda Hart.

First name: ________ Surname: ________ Subject: ________ (N)

First name: ________ Surname: ________ Subject: ________ (E)

First name: ________ Surname: ________ Subject: ________ (W)

First name: ________ Surname: ________ Subject: ________ (S)

496 TSUNAMI ★★★

The numbers alongside each row or column tell you how many blocks of black squares are in a line. For example: 2, 3, 5 tells you that from left to right (or top to bottom) there is a group of two black squares, then at least one white space, then a group of three black squares, then at least one white shape, then a group of five black squares. Each block of black squares on the same line must have at least one white square between it and the next block of black squares.

Column clues (left to right, top to bottom):

1 1 2 11 | 2 2 1 12 | 3 17 | 7 3 5 | 5 3 2 | 4 2 | 3 1 2 1 | 1 1 1 2 1 2 | 1 1 3 3 1 4 | 1 1 4 3 1 4 | 1 1 1 1 1 2 1 2 | 2 1 2 1 2 3 1 | 4 1 2 5 | 4 1 1 3 3 | 3 1 3 3 4 | 3 2 2 3 5 | 2 1 3 1 9 | 2 1 1 1 2 7 | 1 2 5 5 | 12 1 4 | 2 8 1 3 | 7 1 1 1 | 6 1 3 | 1 1 1 1 3 | 11

Row clues (top to bottom, left to right):

8 10
7 9 2
7 4 1
1 3 5 1
1 2 3 3
1 1 3 2 4
1 1 1 3 7
1 2 1 2 6
2 3 3 4 1
1 5 1
1 1 5 1
1 2 1 3 2
2 3 2 2 1
3 3 2
5 3 1 2 1
3 1 7 1 1
3 2 5 4 2
3 2 8 1
3 2 3 5 1
3 6 6 1
4 2 6 1
4 2 8 1
4 2 6 1
5 4 4 1
5 6 1 2

Sometimes it is possible to tell which squares are going to be black without reference to other lines or columns. In the example below, we can deduce that any block of six black squares must incorporate the two central squares:

6 □□□□□■■□□□□

Can you complete this tsunami puzzle, to reveal the hidden pattern or picture?

497 I SPY ★

Watch out King Harold, or you'll be just another sucker! Hidden in the background are 10 arrows. See if you can spot them all.

498 TSUNAMI

The numbers alongside each row or column tell you how many blocks of black squares are in a line. For example: 2, 3, 5 tells you that from left to right (or top to bottom) there is a group of two black squares, then at least one white space, then a group of three black squares, then at least one white shape, then a group of five black squares. Each block of black squares on the same line must have at least one white square between it and the next block of black squares.

Sometimes it is possible to tell which squares are going to be black without reference to other lines or columns. In the example below, we can deduce that any block of six black squares must incorporate the two central squares:

6 ▢▢▢▢■■▢▢▢▢

Can you complete this tsunami puzzle, to reveal the hidden pattern or picture?

Row clues (top to bottom):

	Clue
1	1 2
2	2 2 5
3	4 4 3
4	13
5	1 1 2 3 1
6	2 2 6
7	1 5 3
8	2 2 2 2 1
9	2 5 4
10	2 2 3
11	2 4 3
12	1 1 4 2
13	4 3 1 2 1
14	5 4 3
15	3 7 2

Column clues (bottom row, left to right): 3 2 2 2 3 3 1 6 1 2 4 4 1 5 2 2 2 3 1 2 5 1 1 4 3

---

499 BLACK AND WHITE ★

Put some black in this black-and-white movie by finding and shading the shapes at the bottom, in the screen.

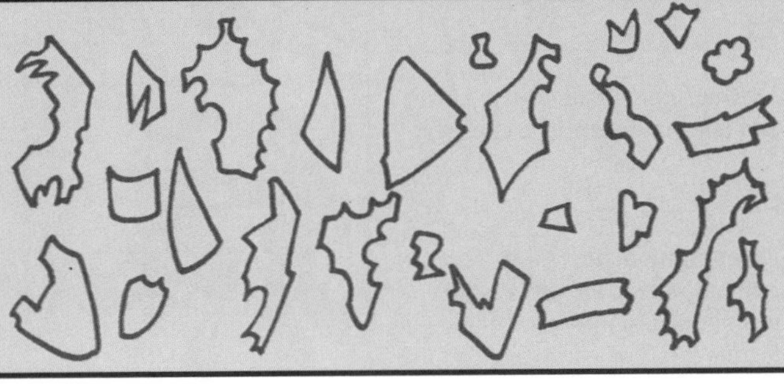

---

500 ARTY ANNIE ★

Look at this simply divine mural that Annie's done. Can you find the continuous black line from the skier's hat bobble to Annie's brush?

SOLUTIONS

1

Pictures B and C are identical. Picture A is different from the others as it has a circular rear view mirror. Picture D is different as it has a couch-like front seat compared to the others which have two single front seats.

2

INSTRUMENT	FORENAME	SURNAME	FROM
BASS	PEARL	HEYER	RHYLL
CELLO	JANICE	TRING	WELLS
HARP	NATHAN	TEWITT	PENGE
VIOLA	HONOUR	HARRIS	DERBY
VIOLIN	DES	KANT	FIFE

3

C		A	B
	B	C		A
A		B		C
	C	A	B	
B	A		C	

4

From the top: C, E, D, B, A, F.

5

1 The piece at the bottom right of the computer; 2 The hands of the clock; 3 The handle to the side of the computer; 4 The plug on the wall.

6

6, K, 9, A, 8, Q, 4, J, 2, 7, 10, 3, 5

7

```
2 9 9 1     5 1 2 7 9     8 3 4 1
1     3     7         0   3       7
2     2 1 5 4 3     1 9 0 6 6 8
4 0 5 7         2 1 2         0
      5 5 8 8     0         6 0 4 8
3 7 5       4 3 1 2 5     1     1
      8 1 0 6         7 8 9 1   7
7 1 5       6 5 4 3 2     5     3
  4 5 6 7 8         6 2 6 2 0 6
  4       1 4 0 7 4 7         3
  4     8         4         3 0 1 7
9 8 3 1 4     4 5 6 8 7     0
  8     8 7 6 5 3     5 4 0 0 0
6     0         2 4         0
7 1 4 2     9 0 1 0 3     5 0 0 0
```

8

9

From the top: F, D, B, C, A, E.

10

6	4	5	3	3	4	5
0	0	6	6	0	3	2	1
3	0	2	5	2	6	4	2
6	1	3	2	2	5	5	1
0	6	0	5	0	4	3	1
5	4	1	6	5	0	2	4	4
4	1	2	1	3	6	1	6

11

FIRST NAME	SURNAME	YEAR DIED	CONVICTION
FRANZ	MULLER	1864	HAT
FREDERICK	FIEWLD	1936	CONFESSION
HERBERT	ARMSTRONG	1922	POISON
HORACE	MANTON	1947	SPELLING
JOHN	HAIG	1949	GALLSTONE

12

C	D	E	B	A
B	E	A	D	C
E	A	D	C	B
D	B	C	A	E
A	C	B	E	D

13

	B	A		C
A	C		B	
	A	B	C	
B		C		A
C			A	B

14

24. One square balances 10 circles and one star balances 14 circles.

15

ACROSS: 1 – 212; 3 – 224; 5 – 415; 7 – 29; 8 – 132; 9 – 634; 11 – 242; 13 – 429; 14 – 11019; 16 – 817668; 21 – 809213; 22 – 59319; 25 – 741; 27 – 588; 28 – 614; 30 – 824; 31 – 13; 32 – 528; 33 – 804; 34 – 657.
DOWN: 1 – 2564; 2 – 226981; 4 – 283; 5 – 4320; 6 – 1241; 9 – 6574096; 10 – 4169214; 12 – 2960; 15 – 1851; 17 – 1981; 18 – 619; 19 – 8455; 20 – 137536; 23 – 9882; 24 – 3828; 26 – 1017; 29 – 110.
The combination is 1941951

16

17

Screwdriver – $2.50; hammer – $10.00; tape measure – $5.50; set square $1.50.

18

```
3 6 8 1 ■ 4 2 5 7
0 ■ 0 2 4 6 1 7 ■ 9
4 ■ 5 0 1 0 9 ■ 8
9 8 ■ 3 8 6 ■ 1 7
■ ■ 8 1 2 3 4 ■ ■
7 0 ■ 1 4 7 ■ 3 5
5 ■ 9 8 9 3 6 ■ 3
0 ■ 1 9 2 8 2 ■ 2
2 2 4 0 ■ 9 3 6 6
```

19

From the top: D, A, E, B, C, F.

20

	A		C	B
C		B	A	
A	B	C		
	C		B	A
B	A		C	

21

28. One square balances 12 circles and one star balances 2 circles.

22

Picture 1 has an extra detail on the butt of the gun. Picture 2 has a sight added to the barrel of the gun. Picture 3 has an extra detail on the helmet. Picture 4 has an extra triangle above the belt.

23

Squares 2a, 5d and 10a.

24

Squares D5, C1, F5, D2 and B1.

25

26

27

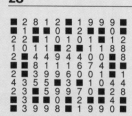

28

```
■ 2 8 1 2 ■ 1 9 9 9 ■
2 1 ■ 2 0 1 ■ 2 ■ 0 1
2 2 ■ ■ 1 0 1 0 1 1 ■ 2
1 0 1 ■ 4 ■ 9 ■ 0 1 ■ 8
2 ■ 4 4 9 4 4 0 0 ■ ■ 8
■ ■ 6 ■ 9 1 1 6 0 0 1 ■
4 3 5 5 ■ 3 ■ 1 0 4 4
2 3 ■ 5 9 9 7 0 ■ 2 8 ■
2 ■ ■ 4 ■ ■ 5 ■ 7 2 ■ ■
■ 3 9 9 8 ■ 1 9 9 0 ■
```

The combination is 8111674

29

30

	C	B		A	
A			C	B	
B		A		C	
	A	C	B		
C	B		A		

31

24. One star balances 6 circles and one square balances 4 circles.

32

1	2	4	5	1	1	1	3
6	2	2	5	6	2	5	3
2	1	2	5	6	3	6	3
2	6	4	5	0	4	0	4
0	3	0	5	6	0	0	0
5	3	6	5	4	4	6	3
3	1	4	1	4	0	1	2

33

34

From the top: B, C, D, A, E, F.

35

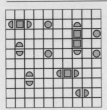

36

37

No. 3, with side B at the top.

38

39

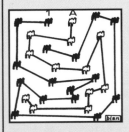

40

2	6	1	4	4	3	0	3
2	3	5	5	6	6	4	2
0	1	0	2	1	1	1	4
5	3	0	0	5	3	0	5
0	6	1	2	1	6	4	1
4	3	3	4	0	5	5	6
2	4	6	3	2	2	6	5

41

42

The five fakes are: the picture of the house, where the gatepost is too tall; the picture of the clown, where the decoration on his hat is too high; the picture of the horse and cart, where the cart's side is too low; the picture of the seagull, where the gull's right wing is too low; and the picture of the ballerina, where part of her skirt is missing.

43

C		A	B	
B		C	A	
	A		C	B
	C	B		A
A	B			C

44

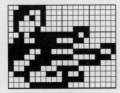

A	B	E	C	D
D	A	B	E	C
C	D	A	B	E
E	C	D	A	B
B	E	C	D	A

45

The matching halves are A and 4, B and 5, C and 8, D and 7, E and 1, F and 3, G and 2, H and 6.

46

1 Flying Fortresses
2 Madame Poll's Parrots
3 Fred the Fire-eater
4 Senor Pedro's Poodles
5 Clever Clowns
6 Agilles Acrobats
7 Crazy Carvellos
8 Jim the Juggler

47

48

5. One square balances one star and four circles balance one star.

49

Nos. 3, 6 and 8.

50

51

No. 1

52

Peter–3, Rick; Alan–1, John; Lex–2, Ian; Dave–4, Fred.

53

The collector chose snail f.

54

55

56

1	2	4	5	2	3	2	3
1	5	6	4	4	2	3	1
1	4	2	2	1	0	3	4
2	5	1	6	5	6	3	3
3	5	4	6	6	2	5	1
0	5	3	6	4	6	1	0
0	4	5	0	6	0	0	0

57

D	A	C	E	B
E	C	B	D	A
A	B	D	C	E
C	E	A	B	D
B	D	E	A	C

58

The combination is 1781786

59

Picture 1 is missing a nail in the fence. Picture 2 is missing a stone on the pavement. Picture 3 is missing a leaf. Picture 4 is missing a brick. Picture 5 is missing a patch on the dog. Picture 6 is missing a nut on the wheel. Picture 7 is missing a leg on the dog. Picture 8 is missing a shirt pocket.

60

Circle = 3, diamond = 6, star = 5 and triangle = 4. Total = 8.

61

```
9 8 7 ■ 2 2 2 ■ 1 2 2
9 ■ 1 0 ■ 4 ■ 5 9 0 ■
1 ■ ■ 2 4 8 ■ 7 0 7
5 5 5 ■ 2 ■ 1 9 4 0 1
■ ■ 9 7 4 1 6 9 ■ ■ 1
2 ■ 2 0 3 1 9 9 0 8 ■ 5
6 ■ ■ 7 8 1 4 5 6 ■ 4
5 1 3 0 5 ■ 5 ■ 2 0 1
2 0 0 ■ 5 2 5 ■ 5 ■ 2
■ ■ 8 1 6 ■ 0 ■ 3 0 ■ 2
8 6 5 ■ 1 7 3 ■ 8 8 4
```

The combination is 2031908

62

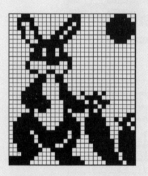

63

64

65

Picture "a" has an extra diamond on the sword. Picture "b" has an extra link in the chainmail. Picture "c" has an extra band on the sword handle. Picture "d" has an extra strap on the sandal.

66

Vases 4, 5, 7 and 11.

67

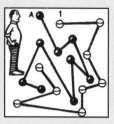

68

The four objects are in squares 4B, 4E, 7B and 6D.

69

	1	2	3	4
A	8	2	11	4
B	3	12	5	7
C	6	10	1	9

The 12 is in square B2 (clue 1). Since neither the 2 nor the 1 is in column 1 (clue 5), neither can be one of the factors of 12 referred to in clue 1. Nor is the 4 in column 1 (clue 4), so the two numbers in question must be 3 and 6. Since the 6 is next to the 10 in the same horizontal row (clue 2), it cannot be in B1, so, from clue 1, the 6 must be in C1, and the 10 in C2 (clue 2), while, from clue 1, the 3 must be in B1, and, from clue 2, the 8 must be in A1. We have placed the 3 and the 10, so, from clue 3, the number in C3 cannot be 2 or 3, nor can it be 4 (clue 7), so, since the highest number in the layout is 12, from clue 3, the 1 must be in C3, and the 9 therefore in C4. Clue 4 now places the 7 in B4, the 4 in A4, and the 5 in B3. Clue 5 therefore tells us the 2 is in A2, and the 11 in A3.

70

From the top:
F, D, B, C, A, E.

71

72

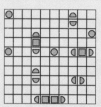

73

F-A-C-D-B-E

74

75

ACROSS: 2 – 622521; 7 – 28762; 8 – 71169; 9 – 1712; 12 – 5097; 15 – 70; 16 – 1232; 19 – 31963261; 23 – 96635970; 25 – 7148; 27 – 99; 28 – 7211; 30 – 1283; 32 – 29040; 34 – 88246; 36 – 598872.
DOWN: 1 – 4840; 2 – 66; 3 – 221; 4 – 272; 5 – 11; 6 – 2673; 10 – 7762392; 11 – 1031598; 12 – 51; 13 – 93294; 14 – 71168; 16 – 16177; 17 – 21302; 18 – 20; 20 – 916; 21 – 299; 22 – 17; 24 – 21; 26 – 1998; 29 – 1940; 30 – 109; 31 – 387; 33 – 45; 35 – 82.
The combination is 21121913

76

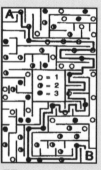

77

Third block on top row, first and third block on fourth row.

78

Weights 1 and 4 will fall, and weights 2 and 3 will rise.

79

80

Snapshot no. 2.

81

The treasure is buried in B5.

82

83

The missing piece is no. 6.

84

	Table 1	Table 2	Table 3	Table 4
N	Harry	Babs	Tessa (dummy)	Fred
E	Susie (dummy)	Kate	Connie	Lola
S	Jane	Roger (dummy)	Dot	Gordon
W	Peter	Alan	Michael	Eddie (dummy)
Contact	2 Diamonds	4 Spades	1 Heart	3 Clubs

85

```
8 1 1 0 1    9      9    2 3 5 0 9
6   3      9  2 3 9 1 6    1      8
0   8    3  1    2    2  3    1
6  0      4 1 0    1    2    3  1
5 0 2 6 4      8 3 5    1 7 9 7 4
        0          2          3  0
2 4 4 1 5      9 1 5 0 5      9
3      3 9 2 6 4      6    3 8 1
8 1 0 8 7 1        6      3 0 4
   9      9 5 1 3 2 6 2
9 2 3 1 6      1 8 2    1 7 6 0 8
0      3    3 8 9 7    3        0
8 7 5 6 2    0    4  2 8 3 9 8
0      5 6 0    5 6 5          0
4 7 0 2 8    7 6 3    4 7 1 1 9
```

86

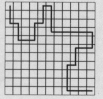

87

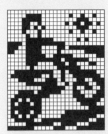

88

89

90

Cube no. 2.

91

The combination is 4121857

92

His painting is no. 2, with side D at the top.

93

1 and 4; 2 and 7; 5 and 8; 6 and 9. The odd-one-out is 3.

94

Pot no. 5. The bottom pot in each column has a lid like the top pot and a label like the middle one.

95

The missing number is 4. In each tile, the lower figure is obtained by multiplying the two digits of the upper number.

96

97

The man bought scarf e.

98

E inner is given as 4, so C inner, which must be an even number (clue 4) cannot be 4 or 8. If it were 2 and D inner 1, from clue 2, B outer and H inner would both be 3 and, from clue 3, the inner 6 could only be in segment G. C outer would therefore also be 6 as would F middle (clue 4). In that case F outer would have to be 12, which is impossible. So C inner must be 6 and D inner 3 (clue 4). So, from clue 2, B outer must be 7, H middle 8 and H inner 7, and since those two H numbers add up to 15, H outer must be 0. With the inner 6 being in C, the outer 6 must be in G (clue 3) and B inner must therefore be 5 (clue 2). To complete the B quota, B middle must be 3. We know D inner is 3, and since, from clue 4, D outer is double D middle, those numbers must be 8 and 4 respectively. F outer must be four times G middle (clue 4) and since the outer circle already has an 8, F outer must be 4, G middle 1 and F middle, from the same clue, 2. To complete their quotas, F inner must be 9 and G inner 8. C outer must be 2 (clue 4) and C middle 7. All inner numbers have now been inserted except in A, which is an odd number (clue 2), so it must be 1. To make up A's quota, the remaining odd numbers must be 5 and 9 and from clue 1, the 9 must be A outer and 5 A middle. Therefore E outer must also be 5 (clue 4) and E middle 6.
In summary:
Numbers given as outer, middle, inner.
A, 9, 5, 1.

B, 7, 3, 5.
C, 2, 7, 6.
D, 8, 4, 3.
E, 5, 6, 4.
F, 4, 2, 9
G, 6, 1, 8.
H, 0, 8, 7.

99

From the top: C, E, D, B, A, F.

100

B	C	E	A	D
D	A	B	E	C
E	D	A	C	B
C	E	D	B	A
A	B	C	D	E

101

D	B			A	C
C	A	D	B		
B		A	D	C	
A	C			B	D
	D	C	A		B
		B	C	D	A

102

Simply turn the bottle upside down and pour wine from another bottle into the recessed dimple and drink it. You have kept your word by 'drinking wine from the bottle'!

103

4. A sister and her brother, both married. One has a son and the other has a daughter.

104

Silhouette 1 is picture f, and silhouette 2 is picture i.

105

Amy – 6; Belinda – 1; Cathy – 4.

106

Tex – 1, Jake; Ian – 4, Fred; Ken – 2, Joe; John – 3, Steve.

107

The four snaps taken at the same time are: top row. first and fourth; and bottom row, second and third.

108

109

110

From the top: D, A, E, B, C, F.

111

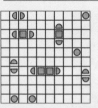

112

2	3	1	4	5	6			6	3	4	2	0	5
5			2	9	5	0	1		7				1
4	0	6	1	3	8			8	9	0	9	9		2
3		5			9	9	3		7		6			5
2		9		5			8		1		4	8		3
9	0	0	1	0	2		4	3	2	9	0	1		8
		8		8		8		8		2		3	0	8
	2		2		0		8	9	3	0	7	1
	4		3	7	1	9	2	4		1		5
3	1	8	8	6			2		3	9	9	2
3		0		1	0	6	1	1	2		0
5	4	3	9	6		3		0		4	3	7	6
2		8		3		5	5	8		8
1	0	3	1		8	0	1		7		1	1	9
5		4		8		3	5	6	0		5

113

B	A	E	C	D
E	C	A	D	B
D	E	C	B	A
C	B	D	A	E
A	D	B	E	C

114

Hotel 1 has 158 rooms (clue 3). Since Perry manages hotel 3 (clue 5), clue 4 rules out hotel 4 as the one with 197 rooms, which is next clockwise from Guy's Castle Hotel, nor does hotel 4 have 203 rooms (clue 2), so it must have 224. Its manager cannot be Guy (clue 4), and we know he is not Perry. Clue 1 rules out Max, whose hotel has fewer rooms than the Majestic, so he must be Rupert. We know the Majestic is not managed by Guy, and clue 1 rules out both Max and Rupert, so it must be Perry's hotel, number 3. So, from clue 1, Max

must run hotel 1, the smallest, which leaves Guy's Castle Hotel as number 2 on the plan. So, from clue 4, the Majestic must have 197 rooms, leaving the Castle with 203. Clue 5 tells us the Excelsior cannot be Max's hotel, so it must be Rupert's, leaving Max's as the Grand.
In summary:
1, Grand, Max, 158 rooms.
2, Castle, Guy, 203 rooms.
3, Majestic, Perry, 197 rooms.
4, Excelsior, Rupert, 224 rooms.

115

116

A		B		C	D
	C	D		A	B
D	A		B		C
	B	C	A	D	
C			D	B	A
	B	D	A	C	

117

NAME	JOB	SUBJECT	PASSES
HUGH	POLICE	BRICKS	5
IVOR	POST	POETRY	3
WATT	SHOP	GRIBBLE	2
WENDY	BAR	SOAPS	4

118

	4			1	3	9	5			1	
8	0	8	5		3	9		1	6	6	1
8		1		1	3	9	8		2		7
8	0	8	5	0			1	3	9	5	7
5		7	8	9	4	3	2	2	5		7
		1	4	1	0	1	6	4	4		
1		6	3	8	7	2	0	6	4		7
9	2	0	5	5			5	0	5	0	9
9		0		6	3	8	7		1		9
8	5	0	4		3	0		1	5	1	2
	2			1	6	0	0			0	

The combination is 14101644

119

Mike – 2, Joan; Rex – 1, Mia; Tom – 4, Jane; Ian – 3, Kate.

120

1 Vase handle 2 Flower stem 3 Castle tower 4 Dog's leg 5 Man's tie.

121

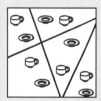

122

Plug C

123

A – 10, B – 4, C – 6.

124

The man chose briefcase e.

125

D	E	C	B	A
E	A	D	C	B
C	B	A	E	D
A	C	B	D	E
B	D	E	A	C

126

127

From the top: B, A, C, D, E, F.

128

5 is the innermost number on strap D (clue 4), so that cannot be the strap referred to in clue 5, nor can strap E (clue 3), or strap C (clue 7), while the outermost numbers on both straps A and F must be single-digit numbers (clue 2), so the strap referred to in clue 5 must be strap B. Clue 8 tells us the 17 is not the innermost number, so, from clue 5, the strap B numbers, reading outwards, must be 12, 1 and 17. So, from clue 8, the innermost number of strap E must be 18, and that on strap F therefore 8. We have now placed four innermost numbers, which total 43, so, from clue 1, the other two must total 21. From numbers already placed, we know these cannot be 18 and 3, 17 and 4, 16 and 5, 13 and 8, or 12 and 9, and clue 6 rules out both 15 and 6 and 11 and 10, so they must be 14 and 7. So, from clue 4, the 7 must be on strap C, and the 14 on strap A. We now know the single-digit number in the middle of strap A (clue 2) is not 1, 5, 7 or 8, nor, since the 15 is not an innermost number, can it be 6 (clue 6). It clearly cannot be 2 (clue 2). If it were 3 or 4, then, from clue 2, one of the other two numbers referred to would have to be 1, but we have already placed that number elsewhere, so, by elimination, it must be 9. We know the number outside it is not 7 or 8, nor, since we have placed 7 and 8, can it be 1 or 2 (clue 2). We also know that it is not 5, and, since we have placed the 5, it cannot be 4 (clue 2), so it must be 3 or 6, and so must the outermost number of strap F (clue 2). But we have placed the only even number on strap F (clue 3), so its outermost number must be 3, and the 6 must be on strap A. We know the 15 is not on strap B, so, from clue 6, it must be the middle number on strap F. Clue 6 now reveals the 10 as an outermost number. The middle number next to it is 16 (clue 6), so they cannot be on strap E, which already has one even number (clue 3), or on C, which has only one two-digit number (clue 7), so they must be on strap D. Since the 2 is not on strap C (clue 7), it must be one of the two even numbers on strap E (clue 3), which leaves the 4 on strap C. Clue 7 also places the 13 on strap C, leaving the 11 on strap E. From clue 3, the 2 must be the outermost number of strap E, and the 13 therefore is the outermost on strap C (clue 7), leaving the 11 and the 4 as the central numbers on their respective straps.
In summary:
(Reading outwards)
Strap A: 14, 9, 6.
Strap B: 12, 1, 17.
Strap C: 7, 4, 13.
Strap D: 5, 16, 10.
Strap E: 18, 11, 2.
Strap F: 8, 15, 3.

129

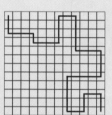

130

6	0	3	8	4	5			7		4	5	7	2	3	
1				8		2	9	4	6			0			9
2	8	8	0	1	6			5	6	8	3	3			0
3		9		8		1	9	3	1		8				0
4		9		6					1		9	2	9		6
9	5	3	4	1		5	1	2	6	3	0				6
		6						8				7	3	4	
	2			2		8		1	4	5	6	3	7		
	9		8	5	0	3	3	7			5		8		
7	2	3	5	3			9		5	3	6	8	1	0	9
	8			6		5	3	6	8	1		0			
4	0	6	6		5		7		2		7	4	4	3	0
9		7				6		1	0	6	4		3		
9	3	8	9		8	1	7			3		5	5	6	0
		9				3		2	5	8	6			0	

131

132

133

134

ACROSS: 1 – 574; 3 – 812; 5 – 535; 7 – 73; 8 – 805; 9 – 565; 11 – 702; 13 – 999; 14 – 79042; 16 – 298124; 21 – 527040; 22 – 54126; 25 – 953; 27 – 139; 28 – 240; 30 – 133; 31 – 41; 32 – 130; 33 – 488; 34 – 780.

DOWN: 1 – 5329; 2 – 479925; 4 – 136;
5 – 5070; 6 – 3504; 9 – 5482262;
10 – 5727060; 12 – 2209; 15 – 9464;
17 – 9152; 18 – 117; 19 – 1951;
20 – 609217; 23 – 4313; 24 – 1930;
26 – 3360; 29 – 438.

The combination is 5121766

135

Treble 18; Double 9; Single 11

136

Alicia, no. 3; Bernadette, no. 8;
Claudia, no. 6.

137

No. 3

138

The extra details are: 6 – shield;
8 – coat of arms; 10 – hilt. The
missing details are: 2 – gate;
3 – knee; 7 – ear; 12 – tail.

139

Same palette and same picture – 3,
5; same palette and different
picture – 1, 6; different palette and
same picture – 2, 4.

140

The man chose t-shirt i.

141

Joe – 4, Jim; Fred – 2, David; Ian – 3,
Kyle; Mick – 1, Jack.

142

From the top: D, B, E, A, F, C.

143

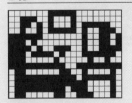

144

A	B	E	C	D
D	A	B	E	C
C	D	A	B	E
E	C	D	A	B
B	E	C	D	A

145

A	B	C		
		B	A	C
B	C	A		
	A		C	B
C			B	A

146

No. 8

147

148

27

149

Plug B should be inserted in the
socket.

150

151

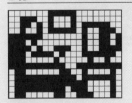

152

A – 3, D – 3.

153

The middle one and the bottom one
in the first column, and the top in
the third column.

154

155

1 – B, 2 – C, 3 – A.

156

157

158

```
2 2 1 5 5 ■ 4 4 4 4
5 ■ ■ 5 0 ■ 8 ■ ■ 4
2 ■ 2 8 8 ■ 4 8 ■ 3
8 1 ■ ■ 2 ■ 1 1 1 1
1 ■ 1 2 6 1 1 2 9 0
■ ■ 2 1 1 7 5 5 ■ ■
2 ■ 4 9 0 6 2 2 ■ 4
2 4 4 ■ ■ 0 2 ■ 1 4
3 ■ 1 5 5 ■ 1 5 9 4
5 ■ ■ 2 ■ 1 ■ 1 9 4
2 2 2 2 2 ■ 1 1 2 3 0
```

The combination is 2111755

159

	B	C		A	
			A	B	C
A	C				B
C			B	A	
B	A		C		

160

7 – 38, 9 – 30, 18 – 47.

161

1	0	3	4	5	1	2	4
6	5	0	0	0	2	3	4
3	1	6	1	2	4	4	6
6	1	5	5	0	3	3	2
6	4	0	4	5	6	3	5
5	3	2	1	3	1	0	5
6	0	1	6	2	2	2	4

162

No. 4

163

From the top: F, D, A, B, C, E.

164

Insects g, d and o are shown in
silhouette.

165

A and D are the pair; in B, the
design on the cap is different and,
in C, the wheel is missing.

166

Weights B and C will rise; weights A
and D will fall.

167

168

169

ACROSS: 1 – 736; 3 – 876; 5 – 252;
7 – 96; 8 – 350; 9 – 786; 11 – 177;
13 – 410; 14 – 25378; 16 – 336393;
21 – 998001; 22 – 94182; 25 – 281;
27 – 855; 28 – 541; 30 – 756; 31 – 72;
32 – 399; 33 – 301; 34 – 894.

DOWN: 1 – 7994; 2 – 695032; 4 – 798; 5 – 2513; 6 – 5077; 9 – 7962925; 10 – 6299081; 12 – 7892; 15 – 5330; 17 – 3798; 18 – 318; 19 – 1898; 20 – 312728; 23 – 4579; 24 – 1559; 26 – 1914; 29 – 420.
The combination is 2721933

170

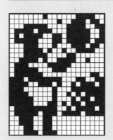

171

172

173

Envelope – 20 cents; pot of glue – 80 cents; pencil – 40 cents; roll of tape – $1.20.

174

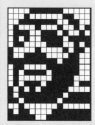

175

176

177

Pictures 2 and 3 are the same. Picture 1 has a pebble missing in the bottom right-hand corner. Picture 4 has an extra window in the sandcastle.

178

```
7 6 2 3     9 1 3 6 9     2 0 3 1
0     0 0         1     9     5
0     3 3 9 0 6     7 0 8 3 5 7
8 0 5 9         9 7 4         4
    4 3 2 8     2         6 3 1 2
3 8 0     8 3 3 0 7     9     5
    1 8 1 0     5 3 6 4     0
9 1 3     3 1 0 1 1     9     5
    8 2 7 1 4     2 1 0 9 5 4
2     3 6 0 6 1 0     3
4     5     5         6 3 0 9
4 4 8 1 5     2 7 3 0 5     5
1     6 6 3 0 2     2     2 0 8 5
0     7     2 9     4     0
8 7 9 0     6 8 4 1 1     8 3 3 5
```

179

The $5,000 prize cannot have been in box 1 or 6 (clue 7) or 2, from which Lynne got a smaller sum (clue 2), or 3 (clue 7 again) or 5 (clue 3), so must have been in box 4. From clue 7, a man opened box 3 and a woman box 5, and since no two men opened adjacent boxes, the remaining two females, Sharon and Susan, must have opened boxes 4 and 5. From clue 6, it was Susan who opened the winner's box 4, while Rob opened box 3, Sharon box 5 and, by elimination, Jim box 1. Both Lynne and Sharon won cash (clue 2), so, from clue 5, the box with the spoon was opened by either Michael or Rob. But, from clue 4, neither Michael nor Jim can have found the soap, so Rob must have done so, leaving Michael with the spoon and Jim with some cash. Therefore, from clue 5, Sharon must have struck lucky with $1,000. Now, from clue 4, Susan was the fifth contestant, and from clue 6, Rob was the sixth. The first contestant wasn't Jim (clue 1), or Lynne (clue 2), or Michael (clue 3), so must have been Sharon. From clues 2 and 3, either Michael or Lynne must have opened third or fourth, so Jim must have been second. He didn't collect 50 cents (clue 5), so Lynne must have done so, leaving Jim with $100, Michael as the third contestant (clue 3), and Lynne as the fourth.
In summary:
1, second, Jim, $100.
2, fourth, Lynne, 50 cents.
3, sixth, Rob, bar of soap.
4, fifth, Susan, $5,000.
5, first, Sharon, $1,000.
6, third, Michael, wooden spoon.

180

Gretchen, who is 6, cannot be number 4 (clue 1), and number 3 is 7 (clue 4). Number 1 is a boy (clue 3), so, by elimination, Gretchen must be number 2. So, from clue 1, the child aged 7 in position 3 is the cowherd's child. Maria, whose father is an apothecary (clue 5), cannot be number 1 (clue 3), so she must be number 4, and, from clue 5, she is 5, leaving the boy in position 1 as 8. So he is not Hans (clue 2), and must be Johann, leaving Hans as the seven-year-old son of the cowherd. From clue 3, Gretchen's father cannot be the butcher, so he must be the woodcutter, leaving Johann as the butcher's son.
In summary:
1, Johann, 8, butcher.
2, Gretchen, 6, woodcutter.
3, Hans, 7, cowherd.
4, Maria, 5, apothecary.

181

182

Plug c is connected to the shaver.

183

Photograph 8 is the one taken of the model.

184

1 The flap on the left-hand porter's clothing; 2 The top leaf on the left-hand plant; 3 The woman's right foot; 4 The bow on the parcel.

185

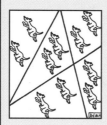

186

Vases 2, 6 and 11 are identical.

187

No. 2

188

189

190

191

Picture a is missing a button on the jacket sleeve. Picture h is missing a rectangle on the label. Picture j is missing a tie. Picture k has part of the newspaper missing. Picture f has a filled-in hat band. Picture I has an extra hook. Picture b has an extra orange.

192

D	A	C	E	B
E	C	B	D	A
A	B	D	C	E
C	E	A	B	D
B	D	E	A	C

193

Beaker – $ 1.20; tube of tooth-paste – $2.50; flannel – $2.00; bar of soap – 50 cents.

194

195

No. 4. In each row, the small rectangle makes a quarter-turn clockwise and the circle moves half as much as that in an anti-clockwise direction.

196

1 Paint-brush on floor 2 Bird's tail 3 Pane in skylight 4 Palette 5 Bird's wing 6 Tube of paint on floor 7 Artist's cravat 8 Picture on floor.

197

C			A	B
	B	C		A
A			B	C
B	C	A		
	A	B	C	

198

6	4	5	3	3	3	4	5
0	0	6	6	0	3	2	1
3	0	2	5	2	6	4	2
6	1	3	2	2	5	5	1
0	6	0	5	0	4	3	1
5	4	1	5	0	2	4	4
4	1	2	1	3	6	1	6

199

Fork, sweet and box.

200

Here's one possible route.

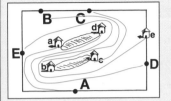

201

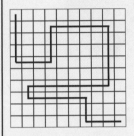

202

1	0	2	6	4		1		3		7	1	6	0	5
3		1		1		5	1	3	0	0		0		7
9		1		0		8		0		9	7	1		1
5		9		8	7	2		0		9	1		0	4
6	3	0	4	4		8	4	9		8	1	4	6	4
		2				2		0		0		8		
2	3	1	0	4		7	3	9	3	0		1		3
6			8	8	9	2	1		9		2	3	3	
9	1	3	3	4	5		2			8	3	0		
	8				5	2	3	4	8	1		1		
2	6	8	6	6		3	1	2		4	1	5	4	4
4			2		6	1	0		2		3			3
5	1	9	0	0		0		3		7	0	2	2	2
2			5	5	0		1	8	3					6
6	3	7	1	5		7	0	6		8	1	9	9	5

203

Poster A shows Jacob (clue 2) and poster D shows Churchman, so Herbert, who's shown on the poster horizontally adjacent to the one showing 'Butch' McColl (clue 1), can't be shown on poster C, nor does poster C show Silvester Jaggard (clue 2), so it must show Matthew. We now know that Silvester Jaggard isn't shown on poster A, C or D, so he must be on poster B. By elimination, Herbert must be on poster D, and, from clue 1, Matthew, on poster C, must be 'Butch' McColl. By elimination, Jacob's surname must be Wolf. So, from clue 3, 'Pony' must be Silvester Jaggard on poster B. Herbert Churchman on poster D isn't 'Apache' (clue 4), so his nickname must be 'Rio', and 'Apache' must be Jacob Wolf on poster A.
In summary:
A, Jacob 'Apache' Wolf.
B, Silvester 'Pony' Jaggard.
C, Matthew 'Butch' McColl.
D, Herbert 'Rio' Churchman.

204

205

The mirror image pairs are: 1 and 6, 2 and 7, 4 and 9, 5 and 8. Figure 3 is the odd one out.

206

The twins are A and C. In B a bolt is missing from the table leg, and in D the chef has hair.

207

Box c is the same as the one being held by the magician.

208

209

Impression 4 was made by the stamp.

210

211

No. 1

212

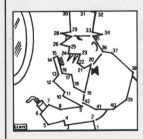

213

Tulip, A – 4; basket, B – 6; shield, F – 1; ice-cream, G – 3.

214

Nos. 2, 4, 6 and 9.

215

216

1 – F; 2 – C; 3 – H; 4 – A; 5 – G; 6 – D; 7 – B; 8 – E.

217

No. 2

218

Nos. 4 and 6.

219

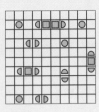

220

From the top: 6 – 5; 9 – 10; 3 – 4; 2 – 1; 8 – 7.

221

The fourth one down in the left-hand column, the bottom one in the middle column and the middle one in the right-hand column.

222

The man with the beard bought a fez. The young man wearing a t-shirt bought a rucksack. The woman wearing the triangle-patterned dress bought a flower hair-decoration. The woman with the circular belt buckle bought a jacket.

The man wearing glasses bought a book. The fair-haired young man in the foreground bought a jumper. The woman wearing the polka-dot dress bought a necklace. The man with the dark wavy hair replaced his tie with a new dickey bow. The man in overalls replaced his shirt with a new t-shirt. The fair-haired man in the roll-neck jumper bought a baseball cap.

223

Tex – 3, Jane; Chip – 1, Hazel; Ty – 4, Kate; Jed – 2, Jo.

224

1 Leaf in the top left-hand corner; 2 Lower window; 3 Circle on the bag; 4 Right-hand root 5 Pocket; 6 Doctor's mirror; 7 Shrub to the right 8 Lapel.

225

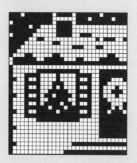

226

		C	B	A
A	C	B		
B			A	C
	A		C	B
C	B	A		

227

A Trish & Zoe   B Ros & Viv
C Una & Xena   D Sue & Wendy

228

The third from the left in the second row down and the second and fourth from the left in the third row down.

229

230

The objects appear in boxes A5, D5, E3 and G5.

231

No. 3 with side b at the top.

232

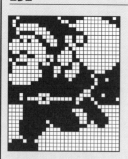

233

6	6	4	4	4	3	6	6
5	0	1	2	5	4	0	2
0	0	3	4	5	2	5	0
1	5	1	1	1	2	5	2
1	4	3	0	6	1	4	3
2	5	5	2	2	3	3	1
6	6	0	3	4	0	6	3

234

```
■ 1 1 9 7 1 5 ■ 2 1 1 6 6 8 9
3 ■ 2 2 0 ■ 6 ■ 2 ■ 1 ■ 3 2 ■
3 4 2 8 7 2 9 ■ 4 3 1 4 8 ■ 0
7 ■ 5 ■ 6 ■ 8 ■ 3 ■ 4 9 8 1
5 2 5 9 ■ 8 5 1 7 0 7 ■ 7 ■ 2
9 ■ 2 ■ 4 0 7 ■ 6 4 6 3 0 3
4 ■ ■ 1 ■ 2 ■ 2 3 7 5 ■ 1 ■ 1
■ 9 7 8 5 2 2 ■ ■ 5 ■ ■ 3 ■ 0
1 ■ 2 ■ 0 ■ 1 6 9 4 4 5 9 ■
2 8 0 6 4 8 ■ 9 ■ ■ 4 ■ ■ 5 ■
2 ■ ■ 2 ■ 0 ■ 3 3 1 ■ 4 2 3 2 5
5 2 3 ■ 4 ■ ■ 2 ■ 1 ■ 4 ■ 6 ■
4 ■ 4 4 5 7 1 7 ■ 6 5 8 ■ 6 ■
6 6 9 ■ 8 ■ 7 7 0 4 ■ 8 8 1 7
3 ■ 8 5 2 3 9 ■ ■ 6 ■ 7 ■ ■ ■
```

235

From left to right: 9, 3, 4 and 11.

236

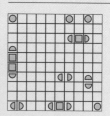

237

238

Nos. 3, 6, 8 and 10.

239

Letter 5.

240

241

Plug c is connected to the toothbrush.

242

The man bought suitcase g.

243

244

No. 2

245

C	E	A	B	D
B	D	E	C	A
E	A	B	D	C
D	B	C	A	E
A	C	D	E	B

246

247

248

4	9	4	9	3	5
8	9	5	2	6	7
5	1	8	1	5	2
8	6	6	9	8	4
1	7	2	3	6	3
3	4	2	7	7	1

249

4	1	1	5	5	5	2	3
1	1	2	6	0	6	6	3
6	4	6	5	0	2	5	6
4	0	3	3	0	5	2	1
6	2	6	4	3	0	2	1
2	4	4	4	1	2	4	5
3	5	0	1	3	0	3	0

250

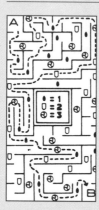

251

The man in seat 13 of row A (clue 6) cannot be Peter or Henry (clue 1), or Robert (clue 4). Judy cannot have a seat numbered 13 (clue 5), so that clue rules out seat 13 in row A for both Charles and Vincent, so, by elimination, the man in that seat must be Tony. Angela is also in row A (clue 1), which must also seat one more woman (clue 3). This is not Nina, who has seat 12 in row B (clue 2), and it cannot be Janet or Lydia (clue 7). Clue 5 rules out Judy, so, by elimination, Maxine must have a front row seat. This cannot be numbered 10 or 11 (clue 4), and we know it is not 13, so it must be 12. Therefore Robert has seat 10 in that row (clue 4), which leaves Angela in seat 11. So, from clue 1, Peter has seat 11 in row B. There must be a second man in that row (clue 3). This is not Henry, who must be in row C (clue 1), and clue 5 rules out Vincent for either seat 10 or seat 13 in that row, which are the only two still vacant. We know Tony and Robert are in row A, so, by elimination, Charles must be in row B. He cannot be in seat 13 (clue 5), so he must be in seat 10. Therefore, from clue 5, Judy must be in seat 10 of row C, and Vincent in seat 11 of that row. So, from clues 1 and 7, Henry must have seat 12 of row C, and Lydia seat 13 of the same row, leaving seat 13 in row B occupied by Janet.

In summary:
Row A: 10, Robert; 11, Angela; 12, Maxine; 13, Tony.
Row B: 10, Charles; 11, Peter; 12, Nina; 13, Janet.
Row C: 10, Judy; 11, Vincent; 12, Henry; 13, Lydia.

252

```
4 2 7 8 9 4     2 3 7 8 1 0
3       7 3 6 0 6     9       5
9 3 3 3 2 1       5 0 0 2 1   0
0   0   8   5 9 8   2   3   9
1   1   0       0   9   8 1 3
3 8 2 4 1 2   5 5 2 6 0 9   0
  8       3 0           2 3 7
  1   4   9   1 8 3 1 3 4
  1   6 3 5 0 8 1     2   5
8 1 8 3 4       2       7 9 1 0
  8     0   8 0 8 3 3 4   0
4 8 2 9 8   2 4     6 3 6 2
0   3     6   7 2 9 0     3
1 3 9 0   6 1 2     3   7 0 6
4   6     0   1 2 4 3       6
```

253

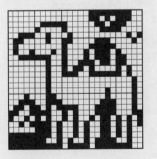

254

John – 4, Joan; Fred – 3, Jane; Mike –2, Mia; Liam – 1, Kate.

255

Vases e and k are identical.

256

1 Castle's turret; 2 Arrow; 3 Bush under tree; 4 Patch on trousers; 5 Feather in cap; 6 Mountain on the left; 7 Castle's gate; 8 Boy's arm.

257

Tangles 1 and 3 will knot, but 2 and 4 won't.

258

1 There are two moons; 2 Right-hand sleeve of nightgown missing; 3 Door of right-hand caravan not in line; 4 Square wheel on car; 5 Steering-wheel in the middle of the car.

259

Go from 1 to: 6 – 3 – 8 – 7 – 5 – 6 – 8 – 5 – 6.

260

261

Pieces 2 and 3 are part of the main picture.

262

Fragments 1 and 4 complete wheel A, and 2 and 3 complete wheel B.

263

The objects appear in squares b6, d4, d6 and g4.

264

265

The identical twins are C and F.

266

A		B		C
	C	A		B
B			C	A
C	B		A	
	A	C	B	

267

268

Paul Hand was Esther's partner (clue 4), so Martina must have been partnered by Richard. So he held the Ace of Hearts (clue 2). Therefore, from clue 1, Ruff had the Ace of Diamonds in the North hand. We now know Paul Hand did not have the Aces of Diamonds or Hearts, and it was a woman who was in the West seat with the Ace of Spades (clue 3), so Paul must have had the Ace of Clubs. So he was not South (clue 5). We know he was not North, and he cannot have been West (clue 3), so he must have been East, and Esther was therefore West, who had the Ace of Spades (clues 3 and 4). By elimination, Richard, who we know was not North, must have been South, and Ruff, in the North seat, was therefore Martina. Esther's surname is not Tenace (clue 3), so it must be Trick, leaving Tenace as Richard.
In summary:
North, Martina Ruff, Ace of Diamonds.
East, Paul Hand, Ace of Clubs.
South, Richard Tenace, Ace of Hearts.
West, Esther Trick, Ace of Spades.

269

The central letter is T (clue 2), so the O referred to in clue 3, which must be in the top row, cannot be immediately above it (clue 2), nor can it be in any of the first, second or fourth squares in the top row (clue 3), so it must be in the right-hand square. So, from clue 3, a P is immediately right of the T, and an A immediately below th T. So, from clue 6, one of the Ns must be immediately to the left of the T, and another N must be diagonally above left of the middle row A (clue 6). This fact rules out the first two squares of the middle row and the right-hand end square for the A, and we have placed letters in the third, fourth and fifth, so the A must be in the sixth square, immediately below the

O, which places an N immediately to the left of the latter (clue 6). We have now placed two As, two Ns and one P and the two Es are both in the same row (clue 7), so the identical letters referred to in clue 5 must be the remaining two Os. The two Es in the same row cannot be the first and second letters of the top row, whose other letters are all in place (clue 1), nor can they be the first or last letters of the middle row (clue 4), which leaves only one square available in that row, so they must both be in the bottom row. But they cannot occupy the two last squares of that row either (clue 1), so one of them must be in its second square. Since the third square of the middle row contains an N, the pairing N P (clue 8) cannot be in the two remaining top row squares (clue 1), and we know one of the two unfilled squares in the bottom row contains an E, so, by elimination, the N must be in the first square of the middle row, and the P in the second. The L cannot be in the right-hand end square of the middle row, nor can it be in the bottom row (clue 10), so it must be in the top row, but, if it were in the second square, the A would have to be in the third (clue 6), which clue 10 denies, so the L must be in the third square, and the A therefore in the second (clue 6). Clue 10 now places the B at the right-hand end of the middle row. So the other letter in the bottom row, along with the second E, must, by elimination, be the R. This cannot be in the right-hand end square, where it would complete the word Oar reading downwards (clue 9), so it must be in the fourth square, and the E in the one to its right.
In summary:

O	A	L	N	O	
N	P	N	T	P	A	B
O	E	A	R	E	

270

271

From the top: C, E, A, D, B, F.

272

4	+	5	÷	9	=	1
x				x		x
6	÷	2	−	1	=	2
÷				−		−
3	+	7	−	8	=	2
=		=		=		
8		3		1		

273

Piece no. 2.

274

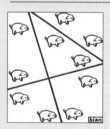

275

Weights 1, 2 and 5 go up, and weights 3 and 4 go down.

276

Pyramid 1.

277

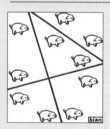

278

End no. 4.

279

Triangle, ladder, butterfly.

280

1 Damien 2 Arthur 3 Colin 4 Errol 5 Ben

281

Fragments 1 and 3 complete wheel A.

282

283

Plug D

284

Letter no. 4

285

The ball between the book and the teddy bear, underneath the pencil.

286

The painting is no. 2 and side C should be at the top.

287

Across: Spade + Club = 15 (row 4), so Diamond = 7 (row 1); thus Heart = 4 (row 2), Spade = 8 (row 3) and Club = 7 (row 4).
Down: Heart + Diamond = 25 (column 1), so Club = 15 (column 3); thus Spade = 12 (column 4), Diamond = 15 (column 2) and Heart = 10 (column 1).

288   289

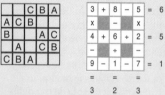

3	+	8	−	5	=	6
x		−		x		
4	+	6	÷	2	=	5
−		÷				
9	−	1	−	7	=	1
=		=		=		
3		2		3		

290

291

292

293

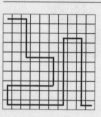

294

295

2	3	7	1	6
9	1	9	4	9
9	8	5	9	6
2	4	0	6	9
9	7	3	3	6

296

297   298

299

Tangles B and D will knot.

300

The details missing are: a) Button on shirt, b) Handle on bag, c) Label on washing machine, d) Collar on shirt, e) Water drop, f) Part of screwdriver, g) Peg on line, h) Button on overalls.

301

302

The identical karts are 2 and 6.

303

1–12, 2–11, 3–16, 4–15, 5–13, 6–10, 7–9, 8–14.

304

305

Wire A leads to the hoverboat, wire B leads to the ship, wire C leads to the car.

306

307

Tony is flying kite B. Jo is flying kite C. Pete is flying kite A.

308

Rope 4

309

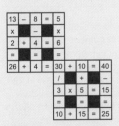

310

13	−	8	=	5
x		−		x
2	+	4	=	6
=		=		=
26	+	4	=	30	+	10	=	40
				/		+		
				3	x	5	=	15
				=		=		=
				10	+	15	=	25

311

312

	C	A		B
A		B	C	
B	A	C		
	B		A	C
C			B	A

313

B		A	C	
	C	B		A
A		C		B
C	B		A	
	A		B	C

314

10	21	23	7	4
25	1	18	13	16
5	14	20	9	2
8	11	6	22	19
15	24	3	17	12

315

316

```
   5 1 0 1 7 9     4 7 4 8 0 3 8
 2   7   8   3     2   1       0
 5 3 6 0 3 0 1     3 4 0 5 2   1
 1   3     3   1       4 4 2 1
 6 9 0 9     4 5 0 1 0 3     3 3
 0   8     8 8 2     8 2 4 9 1 6
 1     1   5   3 7 7 2     4   6
     3 0 9 9 1 0       6   3 3
   6   2     2   1 3 8 5 0 0 2
 6 1 1 6 8 3   0       6   3
 0     5       1 2 5   4 2 1 6 6
 5 8 4   2     2   7   8 5
 5   5 9 9 1 2 6   7 1 3   2
 4 2 0     8   9 5 0 1   5 0 5 5
 4   6 1 5 1 9     8
```

317

318

C	A	D	E	B
A	B	E	D	C
B	D	A	C	E
E	C	B	A	D
D	E	C	B	A

319

Josie's pet is a puppy (clue 5). Julie's cannot be a budgie (clue 4), or a tortoise (clue 3), so it must be a cat. So she is not the girl in position 4, who has a budgie (clue 5). This fact also rules out Josie as girl 4, and clue 1 rules out Jenny, so it must be Jemima who is in position 4. By elimination, the tortoise must belong to Jenny. Since Jemima is in position 4, Julie cannot be in position 3 (clue 3). Nor can she be in position 2 (clue 4), so she must be in position 1. So, since Julie's pet is the cat, Josie cannot be in position 2 (clue 2). Therefore she must be in position 3, and position 2 must be occupied by Jenny. Clue 5 now tells us Josie is ten. Julie cannot be eight (clue 4), or nine (clue 3), so she must be eleven. Jenny cannot be nine (clue 1), so she must be eight, leaving Jemima as the girl aged nine.

In summary:
1, Julie, 11, cat.
2, Jenny, 8, tortoise.
3, Josie, 10, puppy.
4, Jemima, 9, budgie.

320

Mitzi–B, Fritzy–C and Bitzy–A.

321

1 F–5G, 2A–3E, 4A–6F, 3C–4D, 5C–9F and 1A–9B.

322

323

1–E, 2–D, 3–A, 4–B, 5–C.

324

325

326

327

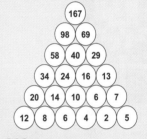

328

329

330

331

C

332

4 and 5

333

D

334

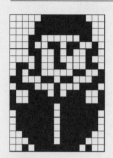

335

336

337   338

1	6	3	6	0	6	0	2
6	2	2	6	6	1	3	5
2	4	1	2	4	4	5	0
0	5	5	3	0	4	0	3
4	1	3	1	4	5	3	3
1	5	0	0	1	6	4	2
6	2	3	2	1	4	5	5

A	B	C	
		A	B	C
C		B		A
		A		C	B
B	C		A	

339

340

The children have the following number of sweets: David=15, Tony=14, Sally=8, Simon=7, Katie=4, Philip=2. Altogether the children have 50 sweets.

341

C	E	A	B	D
B	D	E	C	A
E	A	B	D	C
D	B	C	A	E
A	C	D	E	B

342

From the top: A, B, C, D, E, F.

343

Earth, Jupiter, Pluto, Venus, Mercury, Saturn, Uranus, Mars.

344

B

345

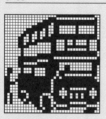

346

8, 3, 10, 2, 7, 1, 11, 4, 9, 6, 5.

347

348

This puzzle does not need any solution.

349

1	0	3	4	5	1	2	4
6	5	0	0	0	2	3	6
3	1	6	1	2	4	4	4
6	1	5	5	0	3	3	2
6	4	0	4	5	6	3	5
5	3	2	1	3	1	0	5
6	0	1	6	2	2	2	4

350

The clocks add on an hour and ten minutes each time, so the final clock will show the time as half past twelve.

351

C	B	D	E	A
B	A	E	D	C
E	D	A	C	B
A	E	C	B	D
D	C	B	A	E

352

The blue box contains 58 items (clue 2), and the green box contains the screws (clue 3), so the 43 nails, which are not in the brown box (clue 1), must be in the red one. We know the green box does not contain 43 or 58 items, and clue 3 rules out 65, so it must contain 39 screws. So, by elimination, the contents of the brown box must be 65 items. These are not washers (clue 3), so they must be carpet tacks, and they are in box C (clue 4), which leaves the blue box containing 58 washers. The green box cannot be box D (clue 3), since it has two neighbours, so that clue places it as box B, and the blue box containing the washers must be box A (also clue 3), leaving the red box as box D.

In summary:
A, blue, 58 washers.
B, green, 39 screws.
C, brown, 65 carpet tacks.
D, red, 43 nails.

353

Since machine B was used by the lady with the red and white costume (clue 5), clue 4 rules out machine D for Euphemia Ponsonby, who hired a machine next but one to the one used by the lady in the orange and white costume. Since Miss Langthorpe used machine C (clue 2), Euphemia's

machine must have been either A or B. Therefore Lavinia's must have been B or C (clue 4), so she did not use machine D either. Nor, since we know Miss Langthorpe used machine C, can Bertha have changed in machine D (clue 1). Therefore, by elimination, Victoria must have done so. So her surname cannot have been Marchbanks (clue 1). We know it was not Ponsonby or Langthorpe, so it must have been Carstairs, and her costume was therefore green and white (clue 3). Therefore Euphemia cannot have used machine B (clue 4), and, as we have seen, she must therefore have changed in machine A, which leaves machine B as the one used by Miss Marchbanks. So, from clue 1, Bertha must have been Miss Langthorpe in machine C, and, from clue 4, Lavinia was Miss Marchbanks who used machine B. Clue 4 also identifies Bertha Langthorpe, in machine C, as the lady in the orange and white bathing-suit, so, by elimination, Euphemia Ponsonby must have worn the blue and white striped one.

In summary:
A, Euphemia Ponsonby, blue and white.
B, Lavinia Marchbanks, red and white.
C, Bertha Langthorpe, orange and white.
D, Victoria Carstairs, green and white.

354

355

The green mailbox cannot belong to number 228 or number 234 (clue 1), and the one at number 232 is blue (clue 4), so the green one must be at number 230. Arlene cannot live at 228 (clue 2), and, since her box is yellow (clue 2), this rules out numbers 230 and 232, so her home must be number 234. Now, by elimination, Mrs Baron's red mailbox (clue 3) must be at number 228. So, from clue 1, Mrs Gerber must live at number 232, and Gemma must be Mrs Baron at number 228. Arlene is not Mrs Fishbein (clue 2), so she must be Mrs Flint, leaving Mrs Fishbein at number 230. From clue 4, Louise is not Mrs Gerber, so she must be Mrs Fishbein, leaving Mrs Gerber as Kate.

In summary:
228, Gemma Baron, red.
230, Louise Fishbein, green.
232, Kate Gerber, blue.
234, Arlene Flint, yellow.

356

9.00, Roland Brake, hill start, Church Hill.
9.30, Helen Weales, reversing, Balmoral Close.
10.30, Rex Chance, parking, Mill Road.
11.00, Ron Gear, emergency stop, Hawthorn Way.
11.30, Vera Swerve, signalling, Market Street.

357

358

C and E.

359

A1 and C2, B1 and A7, F1 and D7, G1 and D2, A2 and A5, C4 and E7.

360

361

D	E	C	B	A
E	A	D	C	B
C	B	A	E	D
A	C	B	D	E
B	D	E	A	C

362

363

Since the figure 5 is not printed in brown (clue 1), the brown stamp must be the 10 cents value. This cannot be stamp 4 (clue 2), so that stamp, which has a 1 in its value panel (clue 3), must be the 15 cents value. So, from clue 4, stamp 2 must be blue. Clue 2 now tells us the cathedral design, which has a zero in its value, cannot be stamp 4, so it must be stamp 2, and, from that clue, stamp 1 must be the brown 10 cents value. The same clue reveals the value of the blue stamp 2 as 50 cents. Now, by elimination, stamp 3 must be the 25 cents value. The mountains are not the design on the 10 cents stamp in position 1 (clue 5), and the same clue tells us they cannot be on the 25 cents value, since we know the 50 cents stamp has a blue frame. We know they are not on the 50 cents value either, so they must be the design on the 15 cents stamp, number 4. Therefore, from clue 5, the red frame belongs to the 25 cents stamp, leaving the 15 cents value as the green stamp. Clue 3 tells us stamp 3 does not depict the harbour, so its subject must be the waterfall, leaving the harbour as the design on stamp 1, the brown 10 cents value.

In summary:
1, harbour, 10 cents, brown.
2, cathedral, 50 cents, blue.
3, waterfall, 25 cents, red.
4, mountains, 15 cents, green.

364

The boy in the red sweater was not Danny or Lewis, who had the chocolate bar (clue 4), and Kevin's sweater was blue (clue 1), so the red sweater must have been Simon's. The first friend met did not have the red sweater (clue 4), or the blue one (clue 1), and number 3 wore the beige sweater (clue 2), so number 1 must have been in the green one. So, from clue 3, it was boy 2 who was eating a banana. We know his sweater was not beige or green, and he was not Simon, in the red sweater (clue 3), so he must have worn the blue sweater, and is therefore Kevin. So, from clue 1, boy 1, in the green sweater, was eating a lollipop. This rules out Kevin, Lewis and Simon, so he must have been Danny. By elimination, Simon must have been eating an apple, and

Lewis must have been the third friend Tommy met, wearing the beige sweater, which leaves Simon as friend number 4.

In summary:
1, Danny, green, lollipop.
2, Kevin, blue, banana.
3, Lewis, beige, chocolate bar.
4, Simon, red, apple.

365

Benedict Marshall, announcer, 8 years.
Denzil Banks, baggage handler, 6 years.
Lawrence Adamson, traffic controller, 7 years.
Matthew Ledger, security guard. 4 years.
Quentin Forrest, electrician, 5 years.

366

367

368

369

2, 10, 3, 12, 4, 7, 11, 5, 9, 1, 6, 8.

370

Tom has a violin, Dick a trumpet and Harry a drum.

371

372

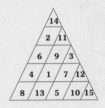

373

374

375

Rosalind painted in oils (clue 2), so the watercolour painting of the windmill, which was not by Nadine (clue 3), must have been done by Josephine, leaving Nadine as the artist who used pen and ink. So she did not draw the pond (clue 4), and must have depicted the village church, so she is Ms Frame (clue 1). By elimination, Rosalind's oil painting must be of the pond. Her surname is not Canvass (clue 2), so it must be Pallett, leaving Canvass as the surname of Josephine.

In summary:
Josephine Canvass, windmill, watercolour.
Nadine Frame, village church, pen and ink.
Rosalind Pallett, pond, oils.

376

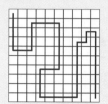

377

378

A=6, B=4, C=5, D=8, E=7, F=3, G=2, H=1.

379

No. 4.

380

381

Buffalo

382

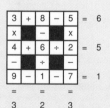

383

384

385

1B–4B, 2B–5D, 2D–9D, 7D–9A, 6A–5G, 3D–6D

386

Moth G has the same pattern on its wings as the bark of the tree, so it will be camouflaged.

387

Owls 4 and 6.

388   389

2	3	7	1	6
9	1	9	4	9
9	8	5	9	6
2	4	0	6	9
9	7	3	3	6

390

391

2–A, 4–D.

392

24

393

Susan's surname is Niven (clue 4) and Knight is the quiz host (clue 2), so Laura the newsreader (clue 3) must be Robins, and Knight's first name must be Donna. By elimination, Susan Niven must be the presenter. She didn't train to be a nurse (clue 4) or a teacher (clue 5), so must have trained as a solicitor. Donna Knight didn't train to be a teacher (clue 1), so must have trained as a nurse, leaving newsreader Laura Robins as the former student teacher.

In summary:
Donna Knight, quiz host, nurse.
Laura Robins, newsreader, teacher.
Susan Niven, presenter, solicitor.

394

Johnny is number 3 (clue 3). Number 1 cannot be Darren Poole (clue 2), or Shaun (clue 1), so he must be Garry. So, from clue 4, boy number 2 must have green boots. Those of lad number 4 cannot be red (clue 1), or brown (clue 2), so they must be black. So, from clue 4, Johnny, in position 3, must be Waters. Shaun's surname is not Brook (clue 1), so it must be Burne, leaving Garry's as Brook. So Shaun is not in position 2 (clue 3), and must be lad 4, wearing the black boots. By elimination, this leaves boy 2, in the green boots, as Darren Poole. So, from clue 2, the brown boots must belong to the lad in position 1, Garry, leaving Johnny Waters wearing the red boots.

In summary:
1, Garry Brook, brown.
2, Darren Poole, green.
3, Johnny Waters, red.
4, Shaun Burne, black.

395

C1 and A4.

396

397

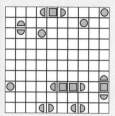

398

399   400

401

$9 \times 8 - 7 \div 5 + 1 \div 7 \times 3 = 6$

402

403

The 19 in B3 is row 3's only two-digit number (clue 2), so the 9 cannot be in any of rows 1, 3 or 4 (clue 3), while the only single-digit number in row 2 is the 7 (clue 2), so the 9 must be in row 5, but not in square E5 (clue 3). Since the 11 is in row 4 (clue 6), clue 5 rules out the 16 for A4, so the 9 cannot be in A5. Nor can it be in C5 (clue 8). Since the 17 is in column D (clue 7), clue 5 rules out the 12 for E5, so, from clue 3, the 9 cannot be in D5, and, by elimination, must be in square B5. Therefore, from clue 3, the 16 must be in B4, and the 12 in C5. There must be exactly one zero in each row and each column (clue 1). We know the one in row 5 is not in B5 or C5, nor can it be in D5 (clue 7), or E5 (clue 5), so it must be in A5. The 1 in row 5 (clue 9) cannot be in E5, since the 6 is in row 1 (clues 5 and 9), so, by elimination, it must be in D5. The 17 in column D cannot be in D1 or D4 (clue 7), and clue 2 rules out D3. Therefore it must be in D2, and D1 therefore contains a zero (clue 7). The zero in row 3 cannot be in A3, C3 or D3 (clue 1), and we know it is not in B3, so it must be in E3. Clue 1 now rules out A4, D4 and E4 for the zero in row 4, which therefore must be in C4. The one in column B cannot be in B1 (clue 1), so it must be in B2. Clue 6 now places the 11 in E4, and the 5 in D4, so, from clue 7, the 8 must be in D3. The number in E5 cannot be any of 16 to 20 (clue 5), and we know it is not any of 1, 5, 6 (clue 9), 7 (clue 2), 8, 9, 11 or 12, so it must be one of 2, 3, 4, 10, 13, 14 or 15. Clue 5 rules out 3, 4 and 14, since we have placed 8, 9 and 19, and also rules out 2, 10 or 13, since we know none of 1, 9 or 12 is in C2, so, by elimination, 15 must be in E5, and, from clue 5, 20 must be in A4, and 14 in C2. Since the numbers in column E total 45 (clue 4), those in E1 and E2 must total 19. Therefore, since we have placed the 12, the 7 cannot be in E2, and therefore must be in A2 (clue 2). Now, from clue 4, the 13 must be in E2, so, from that clue, E1 must contain the 6. The 3 cannot be in C3 (clue 8), so, from clue 10, it must be in A3, and the 10 in A1. The 18 is not in C1 or C3 (clue 8), so it must be in B1. Clue 6 now places the 2 in C1, and the 4 in C3.

In summary:

	A	B	C	D	E
1	10	18	2	0	6
2	7	0	14	17	13
3	3	19	4	8	0
4	20	16	0	5	11
5	0	9	12	1	15

404

405

406

8	2	6	1
6	4	1	5
1	8	5	2
4	6	3	8

407

408

From clue 5, the 1 cannot be in column 1 or column 5, and, since there are no two-digit numbers in columns 1 or 4 (clue 1), the 1 cannot be in column 2 or column 3 (clue 5), so it must be in column 4. But it cannot be in B4 (clue 6), so it must be in D4. So, from clue 5, the 12 must be in C5, and the 10 in E3. The 8 is directly above the 13 (clue 7). This cannot be in column 1 or column 4 (clue 1), nor, since the 13 cannot be in square D2 (clue 1), can they be in column 2 either. Nor can the number 13 be in E5 (clue 4), which rules out column 5. Therefore, from clue 7, the 8 must be in A3, and the 13 in C3. So, from clue 4, square E5 must contain the 7. The 11 cannot be in column 1 or column 4 (clue 1), nor can it be in square A5 (clue 1), so it must be in column 2. But it cannot be in D2 (clue 1), so it must be in B2. The 9 is not in a corner square (clue 2), which leaves only squares B4, C1 or D2. But it cannot be in B4 or D2 (clue 6), so it must be in C1. Since the 6 is directly below the 2 (clue 3), it cannot be in D2, B4, A1 or A5, so it must be in E1. The 2 is therefore in A1 (clue 3). The remaining numbers to be placed are 3, 4 and 5. So, from clue 6, the 5 must be in B4 and the 3 in D2, which leaves the 4 in A5.

In summary:

	1	2	3	4	5
A	2		8		4
B		11		5	
C	9		13		12
D		3		1	
E	6		10		7

409

410

The missing items are: the cushion, the goldfish bowl, the doll, the model ship, the clock and the shelf. The damaged item is the guitar, which has a broken ring.

411

Nos. 3 and 5.

412

1 The model's left hand is out of alignment with her arm; 2 The top of the yacht in the picture; 3 The edge of the frame of the right-hand picture is missing; 4 The artist's overall is uneven at the back; 5 The tube of paint has two tops; 6 The paint-box base is longer that its lid; 7 The model's left foot; 8 The wall-floor division is too high (between the model's calves); 9 One of the paint-brushes is outside the jar; 10 The table has only two legs.

413

Weights A and B will rise, and weights C and D will fall.

414

1 Window of spaceship; 2 Alien's antenna; 3 Bottom rung of ladder; 4 Door of spaceship.

415

416

John=Train, Joe=Ball, Sue=Doll.

417

The Fallaboutlaughing Show liked the video of Trev's little sister falling out of bed best!

418

419

Oxford

420

421

N	F	Y	K	C
Q	J	W	H	T
G	U	R	B	M
A	L	D	V	O
X	P	I	S	E

422

423

Monday, plumber, "Hello", "Buzz off!".
Tuesday, aunt, "Who's a pretty boy?", "Get lost!".
Wednesday, TV repairman, "Good morning". "Beat it!".
Thursday, gasman, "Nice to meet you", "Get out of here!".
Friday, sister, "How do you do?", "Go away!".

424

Pen – $3.75; pencil – 89 cents; ruler – $1.20; bottle of ink – $3.95.

425

```
4 1 8 9 2    2   2   9 3 7 2 1
3   1   3    5 2 0 4 9   5     6
9   5   7    3   2   2   8     9
1   5   7 0 5   9   0   8     9
4 1 6 3 6    8 1 4   6 2 2 5 9
        5        3          3   4
7 1 7 0 3        5 0 3 2 6   1
4     1 4 2 6 8   7   9 5 0
8 4 1 0 2 3        4      6 2 5
        0     7 6 4 1 3 2    0
6 2 0 0 8    5 1 3   8 1 6 5 5
1     3   9 8 8   3          9
5 0 3 7 1   1   2   8 9 0 9 3
0     9 7 4   6 8 6         2
5 1 1 6 9    4 5 1   3 9 0 9 2
```

426

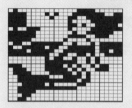

427

Dr Adam – 4, Ian; Dr Felp – 2, Mike; Dr Carn – 1, John; Dr Stern – 3, Joe.

428

429

1. Kate, 2. Brother, 3. Sally and Andrew, 4. Cousin, 5. Great-grandfather, 6. Four, 7. Simon and Bella.

430

B is the book the professor bought.

431

First, Golden Goose, Ava Nother, Railway Approach. Second, Red Lion, Jean-Ann Tonic, Waterworks Alley. Third, Black Bull, Toby Jugge, Mill Street. Fourth, White Horse, Ivor Goodale, Factory Road. Fifth, Green Dragon, Phil Emupp, Gasworks Lane.

432

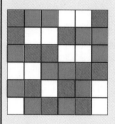

433

A and 7, B and 8, C and 9, D and 1, E and 3, F and 4, G and 2, H and 6, I and 5.

434

435

436

Line A leads to the toy car.
Line B leads to the train.
Line C leads to the duck

437

438

439

440

441

442

443

Monday, mopping, library, television.
Tuesday, polishing, shop, art class.
Wednesday, baking, friend, bingo.
Thursday, washing, sister, whist.
Friday, ironing, hairdresser, choir.

444

The fish which has a seahorse on the left and a jellyfish on the right.

445

Jim has bought picture C, and side no. 4 should be at the top.

446

Tangles 2 and 4 will knot.

447

448

The pairs are 1 and 6, 2 and 9, 3 and 8, and 4 and 7. The odd-girl-out is no. 5.

449

450

451

Box no. 4

452

453

9, 2, 14, 4, 10, 1, 12, 3, 6, 11, 5, 7, 13, 8.

454

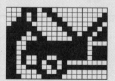

455

456

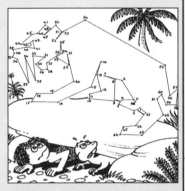

457

First, beach, 25 minutes, bottle top.
Second, park, 15 minutes, spoon.
Third, farmer's field, 40 minutes, toy car. Fourth, own garden, 35 minutes, spanner. Fifth, friend's garden, 20 minutes, doorknob.

458

The values of the shapes are:
circle=1, star=5, square=2.
So the first column adds up to 16.

459

1E–2C, 3E–4A, 2B–7B, 4B–8B,
7F–9G, 3G–4C.

460

461

462

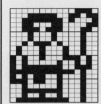

463

Mr Baker, Outlaw, whippet, scared of cats.
Mrs Carrick, Flash, red setter, alcoholic.
Miss Flatman, Eddie, boxer, eats flowers.
Mr McCrae, Tiffany, corgi, anti-social habits.
Ms Scanlon, King, Dalmatian, chases policemen.

464

11

465

4	5	2	6	1	3
2	3	4	5	6	1
5	6	1	2	3	4
3	2	5	1	4	6
6	1	3	4	2	5
1	4	6	3	5	2

466

There are eight polar bears.

467

The identical pictures are B and E.

468

469

Building 1 dates from 1825 (clue 2). Building 3 was not built in 1761, nor is it the station, which dates from 1854 (clues 1 and 4), so it must have been built in 1772. So, from clue 3, building 1 is the windmill. Clue 4 now tells us the tollhouse dates from 1761, which leaves building 3 as the old inn. From clue 5, the Lewis family cannot live there, so their home must be in the old tollhouse dating from 1761. The Vickers family do not live in the windmill or the inn (clue 3), so their

home must be the former station built in 1854. The Carters do not own the oldest building (clue 4), so they must own the windmill dating from 1825, leaving the Mortons at the inn built in 1772. So, from clue 1, the railway station must be in location 4, leaving building 2 as the old tollhouse.
1, windmill, 1825, Carter.
2, tollhouse, 1761, Lewis.
3, inn, 1772, Morton.
4, railway station, 1854, Vickers.

470

471

First, Eric, chicken, lunch.
Second, Alan, pork, morning snack.
Third, Oswald, beef, light supper.
Fourth, Jasper, goose, afternoon snack. Fifth, Percival, turkey, evening banquet.

472

Cup 4

473

474

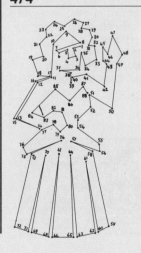

475

476

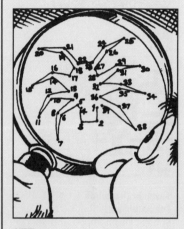

477

Kites: A–Hawk; B–Falcon; C–Eagle; D–Buzzard.

478

479

The shapes can be found: in the kite, the roof of the house, the bird's tail-feather, the grass verge in front of the houses.

480

481

8 stars and 10 tears.

482

483

484

Seven of Diamonds
The hands are:
Straight Flush: 8D, 9D, 10D, JD, QD
Four of a Kind: KC, KD, KH, KS and 10S
Run: 6S, 7C, 8H, 9S, 10C
Flush: AH, QH, JH, 7H, 6H
Full House: AC, AD, AS, 9C, 9H
Two Pairs: QC, QS, JC, JS, 7S
Two Pairs: 6C, 6D, 8C, 8S, 10H

485

Butterflies B and F are identical.

486

The Heart is not the 8 or the Jack (clue 1), and the 5 was a Club (clue 3), so the Heart must have been the 2. So it was not dealt by Charlie (clue 4), or Bevis (clue 1), and Dean's card was a Diamond (clue 2), so it must have been Andrew who dealt the Heart. Therefore it cannot have been card 1 or card 2 (clue 5), and clue 1 rules it out as card 4, so it must have been card 3. So, from clue 1, card 4 must be the 8, and, from clue 5, card 1 must be the Jack. We now know the 5 of Clubs is not any of cards 1, 3 or 4, so it must be card 2. So, from clue 3, the Spade, which we know is not card 3, must be card 4, and it is therefore the 8. Now, by elimination, Dean's Diamond must be the Jack in position 1, and, from clue 4, Charlie must have dealt the 8 of Spades, leaving Bevis as the dealer of card 2, the 5 of Clubs.

1, Dean, Jack of Diamonds.
2, Bevis, 5 of Clubs.
3, Andrew, 2 of Hearts.
4, Charlie, 8 of Spades.

487

60 circles.

488

489

490

Player 3 is bareheaded (clue 2). Player 1, whose surname is Green, is not James, in the floppy sunhat (clue 4), and it is Jacks who has the straw boater (clue 1), so Green must be wearing the flat-cap. Jacks cannot be number 4 (clue 1), and his headgear rules him out as number 3. We know he is not number 1, so he must be number 2, and, from clue 1, Charles must be the bareheaded number 3. By elimination, James must be player number 4. Jacks is not Walter (clue 3), so he must be Donald, leaving Green as Walter. Charles is not Byass (clue 2), so he must be Wood, leaving Byass as James.
1, Walter Green, flat-cap.
2, Donald Jacks, straw boater.
3, Charles Wood, bareheaded.
4, James Byass, floppy sunhat.

491

492

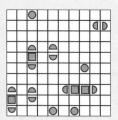

493

494

495

Karen is reading law (clue 2), and Shuffell is studying medicine (clue 4), so Amanda Hart, whose subject is not theology(clue 3), must be reading engineering, and is therefore sitting North (clue 1). So, from clue 3, the theology student is in the East seat. We now know Ruff's subject is not engineering or medicine, nor is Ruff the surname of Karen, the law student (clue 2), so it must be the surname of the theology student in the East seat, which leaves Karen's surname as Diamond. From clue 2, her seat is West, which leaves Shuffell in the South seat. This person is not Petra (clue 4), so she must be Josephine, leaving Petra as Ruff.

North, Amanda Hart, engineering.
East, Petra Ruff, theology.
South, Josephine Shuffell, medicine.
West, Karen Diamond, law.

496

497

498

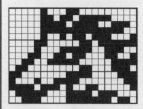

499

500